LET THE EARTH SPEAK

LET THE EARTH SPEAK

Of God's Creation

Editor: Albert A. C. Waite, PhD

MANDRA PUBLISHING

First published in 2001 by
Mandra Publishing
P.O. Box 5136
Riseley
RG7 1GT

Reprint February 2002

ISBN 0 9540429 0 5

British Library Cataloguing in Publication Data.
A catalogue record for this book is available from the British Library.

Printed and bound in Great Britain by
Antony Rowe Ltd
Chippenham
Wiltshire, SN14 6LH

This book is dedicated to my father, Alphonso Carlisle Waite, who, without trying, teaches me something new every time we meet.

COMMENTS

I have found the book to be a good read. It is very informative and the information is presented in a clear and comprehensive way. The book provides pretty convincing comments in favour of the Biblical account of the world's creation.
Sean Morgan (Birmingham)

I thought, even after the first chapter, that it was nice to find a book targeted at my age group, that does not assume that I am 'thick' and know nothing. Everything is explained clearly and understandably, without being patronising.

Not being scientifically minded, I was nearly put off, but I'm glad that I wasn't. I will certainly be adding it to my collection of books when it is published. I particularly found the chapter on the geologic column interesting and how the flood can explain it. I also liked the parts where Bible texts were used to show that scientific discoveries are in keeping with the Bible even if the explanations of the discoveries differ. (e.g. When it talks about the earth's crust being younger than the other layers.)

After reading this book, I wonder how people can believe in evolution and the big bang and not creation and the flood.

My brother, who is 15 years old, has started reading the book too. He is more scientifically minded than me and he agrees that it is well explained, without being patronising.
Louise Lethbridge (Wales)

The book is lucid, readable and quite brilliant. My mining engineering friend is quite happy with the chapter on coal. I like it.
PP (Wales)

I was able to follow this, even though I've only got physics-with-chemistry for school cert. And that was in 1947!! So I think a 17 year old ought to be able to follow it and an intelligent layperson, too! I found it interesting.
M. Dorland (Berkshire)

About the editor
ALBERT A. C. WAITE

Dr Waite is both a scientist and an educationalist. His first degree is in Chemistry. He earned five post graduate qualifications (PGCE, MEd, MA, PGDipCTA and PhD) from three universities: Keele, Reading and Staffordshire. His PhD is in the area of Organo-physical Chemistry.

Dr Waite has taught at all levels of the educational system for a total of 26 years, both in the state and independent sectors, and held the position of Honorary Research Fellow at Staffordshire University. His interest in young people has occupied him outside of the class room for over 25 years, speaking on creation, Bible, education and other topics, both in Europe and the Americas. For over 30 years he has been involved in voluntary organisations, seven of which he has served as chairman (two currently). He is a governor at a secondary school in Berkshire.

Over 70 articles, mostly on science, education and interactions between Bible and science, have carried his name in a variety of journals and periodicals. He also initiated the painting of The Beginning – a synthesis between the creation stories in Genesis and various disciplines of science, which a newspaper described as "A Creation Masterpiece". The work, measuring 17ft x 5ft, which is displayed at Newbold College, Berkshire, England, was jointly designed by Dr. Waite and the artist, Cliff Sellors (deceased).

Dr Waite sees himself as a freelance researcher/writer, among other things. He is married with two teenage children and his newest hobby is feeding Koi and gold fish in his garden pond.

CONTRIBUTORS

All contributors to *Let the Earth Speak* of God's Creation are established writers and each pursues academic and research careers.

Chapter One was written by Albert A. C. Waite, PhD.

Chapter Two was written by Ariel A. Roth, PhD.
Dr. Roth was director of Geoscience Research Institute from 1980 to 1994. His current research involves the study of "termite" mounds in New Mexico. He has devoted 30 years to the study of the interface between science and religion and has conducted numerous field trips worldwide.

Chapter Three was written by Albert A. C. Waite, PhD and Clyde L. Webster, PhD.

Chapter Four was written by M. Elaine Kennedy, PhD.
Dr. Kennedy has pursued research in sedimentology studying lake muds in Wyoming and California. She has also conducted research on a "hadrosaur nest" near Choteau, Montana. She is employed as a Research Scientist by the Geoscience Research Institute at Loma Linda University, and is currently investigating the mudstones and sandstones associated with dinosaur "nests" in Patagonia, Argentina.

Chapter Five was written by Clyde L. Webster, PhD.
Dr. Webster, is a former senior research geochemist at Geoscience Research Institute, where he also coordinated links with educational institutions around the world. He has a deep interest in Radiometric Dating and has been using trace element analysis to characterise ejection patterns of volcanoes in Hawaii and Yellowstone. This research assists in establishing time and source relationships of multiple, ancient volcanic events.

Chapter Six was written by Albert A. C. Waite, PhD.

Chapter Seven was written by L. James Gibson, PhD.
Dr. Gibson is the Director of the Geoscience Research Institute at Loma Linda University. His research includes speciation and biogeography; in particular, the extent of change in species and the worldwide distribution of

animals. His research focuses on endemic species and their migration and provides insight on species distributions before and after the Genesis flood.

Chapter Eight was written by M. Elaine Kennedy, PhD.

Chapter Nine was written by Clyde L. Webster, PhD.

Chapter Ten was written by John T. Baldwin, PhD.
Dr. Baldwin is a professor of theology at Andrews University. His research interests focus on the philosophical relationship between science and religion. He won a John Templeton Foundation prize in 1994, for a paper published in the Harvard Theological Review.

THE COVER

Much thought has gone into the composition and designing of the cover, to make it as informative as any of the ten chapters in this volume.

The black background of the cover represents the darkness that surrounded Earth, after it was created, at a non-empirical time (as far as humans are concerned) – "In the beginning" – before it was developed for human habitation (Genesis 1: 2).

The front is composed of three pictures which, together, depict the three states of matter on Earth that every GCSE or High School student knows exists. They are solid (ice), liquid (water) and gas (air). Furthermore, the rainbow serves as an illustration for chapter ten, written by Dr John T. Baldwin, of which E. W. Marter (theologian and educator) refers to as "This excellent chapter..." The presence of a rainbow on a book with the title: *Let The Earth Speak*, is also a fitting reminder of God's promise that He will not destroy the earth again, with a worldwide flood.

On the back is the third of eight frames of The Beginning, which was co-designed by Dr. Albert A. C. Waite and the artist, Cliff Sellors (deceased). This frame is an artistic presentation of the formation of dry land and seas, by way of a volcanic eruption out of the water that surrounded the earth, up to day three of creation week (see Genesis 1: 9,10).

The cover of this book seeks to present a synthesis (an interaction) between God's work (His world of science) and His word (the Bible) for an informed understanding of Him.

Let the Earth speak – of God's creation.

ACKNOWLEDGEMENTS

This book was conceived while travelling through Colorado, USA, en route to a Biblical Research Institute Science Counsel (BRISCO) conference, at the invitation of Dr. Ben L. Clausen, in 1992. The gigantic uplifts, sparse vegetation, the different layers of rocky strata, the gorges and white waters that entertained me, also compelled me to cry out (even though I was heavily sedated by jet lag): "Let the earth speak of God's creation." Thank you, Ben, for that invitation.

The courage of the other contributors: Dr. John T. Baldwin, Dr. L. James Gibson, Dr. M. Elaine Kennedy, Dr. Ariel A. Roth and Dr. Clyde L. Webster, to support the idea of this book at its germinative stage, is fully acknowledged. While each chapter is credited to its author, I accept full responsibility for any error that crept into its production.

Let the Earth Speak would be of less value if it were not for the critical comments from a number of specialist readers. Although I have not included all the suggestions from Malcolm Bowden, Pastor E. W. Marter, Dr. A. J. Monty White and Dr. Cyril Vesey in this book, their invaluable contributions are graciously acknowledged.

Much appreciation goes to Myrna Dorland and another "much loved and respected, retired teacher in the Watford area" for weeding out many of my flamboyant expressions; to Dr. Jeff Brown for encouragement when the hurdles seemed unassailable, and the many young people in Britain who often ask me for a book that is assertive towards creation and not primarily evolution bashing.

A special thank you to Alicia A. C. Waite, my daughter, who has demonstrated IT, literary and critical wisdom, way above her 15 years, in the preparation of this book.

I should also like to acknowledge:
Dr. Ariel A. Roth for providing camera ready photographs for Fig. 2.1 and Fig. 2.3.
Dr. M. Elaine Kennedy for providing photographs for Figs. 4.1, 4.2, 4.3, 4.4, 4.5, 4.6, 4.7, 4.8, 4.10, 8.4 and 8.5.
Alicia A. C. Waite for drawing Figs. 1.1, 2.2, 4.9, 8.1, 8.2, 8.3, 8.6 and 8.7.

Albert A. C. Waite
Editor

ILLUSTRATIONS

CONTENTS

PREFACE

Sir Karl R. Popper, in his book *Conjectures and Refutations: The Growth of Scientific Knowledge* (Routledge, 1963, p215), says, "I assert that continued growth is essential to the rational and empirical character of scientific knowledge; that if science ceases to grow it must lose that character. It is the way of its growth which makes science rational and empirical..." Karl Popper also maintains that the development of a theory is a creative process and that an idea for such a development has no predetermined starting point.

The idea for this book, *Let the Earth Speak*, came to its editor while he was jet lagged and driving in the back of a car in Colorado; hardly a good frame of mind to be conducive to creativity! During that trip, the chapters of the book and its contributors were determined. The book is not primarily about science. Rather, it is an interaction between God's two books – the Bible (His words) and the world (His works).

All the contributors work extensively with young people around the world. The reader should, therefore, find the ten chapters and information about the book cover refreshingly presented. The referencing style of each contributor is retained. Careful reading will also detect new information, within the field of this synthesis – science and the Bible. That being so, *Let the Earth Speak* contributes to the growth in the rational knowledge of the creation/evolution discussion – a situation Sir Karl Popper would welcome.

Let the Earth Speak presents the information assertively, to synchronise with the mind set of teenage young people, who want to know and speak about origins, creation, God and the Bible, in a positive way and without the need to be defensive, when they discuss these topics with evolutionists. The book, therefore, should have a wide appeal to Christians and non Christians alike.

Albert A. C. Waite
Three Mile Cross
April 2001

19

1

ORIGIN AND STRUCTURE OF THE EARTH

1.1 THE NEED FOR A THEORY OF ORIGINS

The origin of the earth is not commonly discussed in isolation to the other planets of the solar system. Nor is the origin of the solar system commonly discussed apart from the origin of the universe. So, when we are looking at the origin of the earth, it is more convenient to focus on the origin of the larger context in which it is situated – the universe.

Leon Lederman,[1] a Nobel Prize physicist, begins his book, The God Particle, with:

> "In the Very Beginning there was a void – a curious form of vacuum – a nothingness containing no space, no time, no matter, no light, no sound. Yet the laws of nature were in place, and this curious vacuum held potential... A Story logically begins at the beginning. But this story is about the universe, and unfortunately there are no data for the Very Beginning. None. Zero. We don't know anything about the universe until it reaches the mature age of a billionth or a trillionth of a second... When you read or hear anything about the birth of the universe, someone is making it up."

Three of a number of interesting ideas in the above quotation say much about our understanding of the origin of the universe. Firstly, while Lederman points out that in the "Very Beginning there was no time, no matter, no space...", he accepts that in the presence of nothingness the laws of nature were in place. This at first may seem contradictory, but it directs the mind to ask a question such as, "Who or what is behind these laws of nature, which are the scientific laws as we now know them to be?"

Secondly, "there are no data for the Very Beginning." This creates a problem in that it is not scientifically possible to be definite about what happened at or before the beginning of the universe. It is not possible for science to operate without data – information! Any view on the "Very

Beginning" must, therefore, be based on extrapolation (projection into the unknown) which is a mathematical means of saying: "This could be what happened way back there, but I am not absolutely sure."

Thirdly, Lederman's pronouncement: "when you read or hear anything about the birth of the universe, someone is making it up", somewhat summarises the previous two points. Information about the origin of the universe could be nebulous, unscientific, fictitious or belonging to the realm of "guessology!" This may not strictly be the case, but the limitation of science to paint an accurate picture of origins must not be underestimated. All in all, a clear outcome of the analysis of Lederman's views is that the study of origin is not purely a scientific exercise, but one that is based upon theories. This is unavoidable, because of the lack of certainty or information. As a consequence, if questions about origins are to be asked, their possible answers must be based on theories.

Theorising or hypothesising is a fundamental means of attempting to find out what we do not know. It is a kind of guessing what the answer to a problem is then trying to see if your guess is correct. In scientific terms, this is more technically called conjecture and refutation. The scientific method takes the form a) to observe b) to hypothesise on the basis of our observation and c) to experiment to test our hypothesis. Theories on origins cannot use the scientific method, for a) we were not there to observe b) we can only hypothesise on the basis of current facts and c) we cannot test by experiment because we do not have any facts, and therefore cannot replicate the conditions present "in the beginning". So the conditions that prevail in the beginning is anybody's guess! Humankind however, seems to be endowed with the innate curiosity to explore the unknown. This is evident from the earliest moments after a child's birth.

1.2 HUMANKIND SEEKING TO KNOW

The newborn baby responds instinctively to his new environment. He will grasp a finger placed in his palm; demonstrate fright if dropped suddenly; make stepping motions if held around the waist. The baby will follow a finger with his eyes and stare at bright colours. Within a few months the baby will become more inquisitive. He will respond to soft or rough textures, unusual objects; crawl towards encouraging sounds; and by ten months will be seen imitating adults by taking awkward steps in an attempt to walk.

During childhood, the sense of exploration becomes acute: cupboards are explored; trees are climbed; meadows and dales are enjoyed; butterflies are caught; lifts and escalators in tall buildings prove irresistible; donkeys, camels, goats, dogs and cats create new attractions. The child constantly looks away from himself for interests. He is forever finding out about the wider world.

By the early teens, the youngster's friends outside the family become important. Football, swimming, a martial art sport (karate, judo, etc.), music and books occupy most of his time. It is now that the God question becomes more meaningful. He wants to know more and more about God and everything else. This quest for knowledge and discovery of the world will continue for life.

One is never too young, too old, too rich or too poor not to want to find out more. What is the source of this quest for knowledge, this inquisitiveness? What is the source of the chemist's eagerness to find out how the first atoms react, the biologist's zeal to discover the structure of the first cell, the astronomer's ambition to find a spark or the little ashes of the big-bang explosion? Is it an innate, inborn force, or an accidental one that has developed over time? Was there ever a time when mankind was not born inquisitive, with the desire to find out? To guess and refute?

Scientists are constantly experimenting, hoping to find that vital theory which explains everything. The path to such a discovery is never monotonous.

Lederman captures the essence of his colleagues' life-work when he says (paraphrase): The life of a scientist is filled with anxiety, pain, hardship, tension, attacks of hopelessness, depression and discouragement. But these are punctuated with flashes of exhilaration, laughter, joy and exultation, which are generated simply by the sudden understanding of something new and important, something beautiful that someone else has revealed. But the sweetest moments come when he himself discovers some new fact about the universe that he alone knows. The joy is even more ecstatic if the new information brings him one step closer to discovering the "God particle".

In May 1996, after ten years of research, scientists at the European Particle Physics Laboratory (CERN) outside Geneva reported evidence that suggested the first quark-gluon particle might have been detected. This was the closest anyone had got to the God particle. And even then, the universe was purported to be 1-micro-second old when such particles might have first existed. The exhilaration and exultation flowed over into the scientific journals with titles such as, "Has CERN made the stuff of the Newborn Universe?" But there was no certain answer.

This quest for the ultimate discovery of the "God particle" is not an end in itself, but it is seen to be the ultimate requirement to concoct the ultimate theory of the origin of the universe. The God particle is so named because it is believed to be the original particle from which all matter was made, but even the elusive "quark-gluon" combination would be too complex to be called the God particle. Something simpler, that is indivisible or incapable of fragmentation, would have to be the aspirant for the original particle.

1.3   OUR INNATE URGE

On a farm where animals are intensively reared, the pig is born, grows and lives in its concrete bunker. It knows no other life. Yet if one day it escapes, the pig will use its snout to dig up the soil and bathe in the first mud hole it comes across. The hen that is hatched and has lived all its life in its wire cage, if it escapes, will scratch for insects as good as any free-range chicken. An old cow which has never left its pen since birth will swim in a river or pond without any training. When the cow is thrust into the pond, it has no time to learn to swim, but it swims, because it has an internal ability to swim, one that does not require learning. The pig, the hen, and the cow have not had any experience of mud bathing, scratching for insects or swimming; yet the first time in their mature lives they are exposed to the natural environment, they do what innately comes naturally to them, without any training.

In a similar way, as humankind we find ourselves on the earth. As we explore it, become frustrated with our inability to explain the presence of simple things like mountains, valleys, space, a tree, the markings in a piece of rock found on Antarctica but purported to come from Mars, we find ourselves asking simple questions in our attempts to understand our relationship with our environment. Why does it look like this? Where did it come from? Who made it? The questions come from within us. We don't have to be taught to ask questions. We may be taught how to refine or make our questions more complex, but the urge to find out comes from within!

As with the cow, hen and pig, there are some things that we do that are natural to us. These things are innate. We were born with them. But what is the source of our innate tendencies? What is the source of the cow's ability to swim? What is the origin of these characteristics? Is it the same as the answer to the questions, "What is the origin of the universe?" and "What is the origin of life?" What theories are there to help us find the answers? Are we tempted or inclined to look to a Higher Being or an accidental source for the answers? To answer this, we must adopt a theory of origin.

1.4 EVOLUTIONARY THEORIES AND THE ORIGIN OF MATTER

The tendency is for us to want to know about the things around us: Who made them? Where do they come from? Why do they have a certain shape? Where did the first English person live? What did the first house look like? Where did the builder get the materials from to construct it? It is all part of our healthy quest to find out more about our origin and the origins of our environment. However, because humans came on the earth after it was already in existence, any report of how it came into being must be based on theories. These theories will carry the baggage of their authors' interests and views of origins. There is no theory which requires human beings to believe that they have created themselves or the earth or, indeed, the universe. There are, however, a number of evolutionary theories that seek to explain the origin of the earth and the universe as well as the origin of life. How well do they achieve this explanatory objective? Let us look at three theories (one is not about the origin of the universe) that have had varying popularity.

1.5 THE BIG BANG

Lederman and the majority of the scientific world assume the big bang to be the theory that best fits the available facts of the origin of the universe. It states that the universe started out as a singularity, as a pin point of matter with infinite density. It grew into the size of a pea grain, still unrealistically dense. It then exploded, and has become less dense as it continued to expand (the universe is believed to be still expanding).

Scientists have studied the rate of this expansion and have concluded that the explosion could have occurred no more than 10–20 billion years ago. Physicists have tried to explain what happened to the matter in the pea-size universe, but are unable to give any kind of description earlier than 10^{-43} seconds after the explosion.

It is believed that the God particle first existed 10^{-35} seconds after the big bang. What happened while the "pea" was intact and then at the moment of explosion is beyond scientific investigation, as there were no human beings present. Big bang physicists, therefore, do not deal with the real origin of the universe, but with situations sometime after the "God particle", and indeed after the universe came into being, 10^{-43} seconds afterwards.

Although the big bang theory has good support for the most likely way the universe came into being, there are some unanswered questions, some of which seem to be basic. For instance, the universe we observe is lumpy:

galaxies, stars, planets, all surrounded by a smooth microwave background. Scientists are in agreement that both a lumpy universe and a smooth background could not have come from the same starting point: the explosion could not have produced both.

Also, the Plasma Cosmology theory directly challenges the big bang theory. In 1986, in a series of experiments, scientists observed huge galaxies that were calculated to have taken at least 100 billion years to form. The experiments were repeated and the calculation was confirmed. This caused a mental crisis! If the big bang, which preceded all matter, could not have taken place more than 20 billion years ago, then this new find of giant galaxies, requiring 100 billion years to form, simply states that the big bang could not have happened![2] These conflicting reports make one wonders if this is a matter of one theory challenging the viability of another, or the workings of science finding their own level?

1.6 THE STEADY STATE THEORY
In 1920, the Steady State Theory, preceding the big bang, was the brainchild of Sir James Jeans. It was later modified by Sir Fred Hoyle and his colleagues. The essence of this theory is: the universe and space are expanding at a steady (constant) rate, but are not changing in density because just enough matter is being created, continuously, to keep the density constant. This continuous creation of matter goes against the basic understanding of the big bang, which states that no new matter has been produced since the initial explosion.

In 1964, Penzias and Wilson discovered a low intensity microwave radiation coming equally from all directions of the universe. It was the type that would come from something that was hot. This discovery was interpreted as strong evidence for the big bang. As a result, the academic community abandoned the steady state theory in favour of the big bang.

1.7 PUNCTUATED EQUILIBRIUM
(Note: It is recognised that Punctuated Equilibrium is not a theory of origin, it is about the evolution of fossils. It is included here as background information and to prepare the reader for subsequent chapters.)

At one time, the fossil record was interpreted as the backbone of evolutionary processes. Without the fossils, there would be no evidence for the gradual development from lower life forms to higher. Creationist scientists have consistently said that the fossil record does not support evolution. There are too many gaps and no substantial transitional forms or missing links.

After many years of creation scientists pointing out the anomaly of the fossil record and evolution, two scientists developed an evolutionary theory to explain the pattern of the fossils. Niles Eldredge and Stephen Jay Gould, in 1972, argued that the fossil record of any one species of animal takes the following pattern:

1. An ancestral form appears in the sediments as fully formed (no transitional state).
2. At a higher level in the strata, fossils of the same species appear, again fully formed, showing no evolutionary changes.
3. Still higher up in the strata, the species disappears.
4. At a later level in the sediment, what is interpreted as a descendant of the earlier species, appears. It is different, but fully formed.

Eldredge and Gould suggest that the appearance of the species at the various levels represents equilibrium, lasting tens of thousands of years. The gap where no fossils are found represents rapid evolution or punctuation in the sequence. These rapid disturbances are said to occur in small groups. These are encouraged more by geological factors, niches, rather than ecological catastrophes.[3]

The suggestion here is that suddenly the parents disappear and offspring appear with no clear genetic link. This punctuated equilibrium theory is high on philosophy and low on science. It clearly reflects the evolutionary views of its authors and the need to find some evolutionary explanation for the fossil record. Is this theory a good attempt to explain the fossil finds? More on this in subsequent chapters.

1.8   THE REAL ORIGIN

There are two traditional ways of finding answers to the question: Where did the universe come from? or What is the origin of the universe?

Either we seek to understand the universe as it is now, and work backwards (extrapolate) towards its origin (the process of science), or we seek the source of revelation (God) who says all things have their origins in Him. We may, however, seek to harmonise the observations of science with the revelations of the Bible to help in our quest for origins. Many universities and prestigious foundations are actively interfacing science and religion to bring about a greater understanding of the origin of the universe.

In 1994, the John Templeton Foundation launched the Science-Religion Course Programme, "to encourage the teaching of high-quality academic [modules which] focus on the relationship between science and religion." In that same year, the C. S. Lewis Foundation devoted its third triennial Summer Institute, convened at Cambridge University, to discussing the topic: Cosmos and Creation: Chance or the Dance. While the impact of this conference is lasting, it is not ongoing. The Templeton Foundation, however, supports over one hundred modules at universities, colleges, and seminaries around the world, on an ongoing basis. Institutions from the United Kingdom, United States, Canada, New Zealand and Australia are participating in this and other science and religion ventures. In England (Newbold College), the Open University has validated a module with the title: The Bible and Science. Two of the module's objectives are: 1) "To establish the role science and the Bible play in the study of origins", and 2) "To recognise some of the ways Christian scholars correlate their science with their faith". Many tertiary institutions are similarly explicit in their effort to integrate faith and learning. For example, the module Faith and Physics is taught at the University of Toronto, Canada; Creation and Evolution – a doctoral level module, at Claremont, USA, and the objectives of the module: The "New Physics" in Theological Perspective at Princeton, USA include, "How did the universe begin and how will it end?" "Did the universe have a beginning, and if so, did it need a God?" "Is the order of the universe the result of chance, or of design?" Scholars are finding that the harmonising of science with the revelations of Scripture gives a more meaningful estimation of the origin of the universe.

A purely scientific approach does not go much further back than 10^{-43} seconds after the big bang. This is not the real beginning. The real beginning of the universe comes before 10^{-43} seconds, which scientists are unable to describe owing to inaccessibility of information. Scientists do not talk about the state of matter at the singularity – zero time. They simply say, matter at zero time was a very dense lump about the size of a pin point. This substance, they say, came from nowhere, out of nothing, under the influence of no one! How could space and time, matter and energy and all the tangible objects around us come from nothing, accidentally? There are hypotheses attempting to explain the process "from nothing to something", but there is no scientific theory, based on experimentation, that does this adequately. The mathematics at zero point breaks down. It becomes meaningless.

Meaningless? Yes, because science can deal only with what is there, the physical universe. Stephen Hawking in his book: *A Brief History of Time*[4], attempts to answer the question, "What happened before the big bang?" with "It is like asking for a point one mile north of the North Pole." If we take another perspective on the earth, a non-myopic one, the question is answerable. Since the earth is an object in the known universe, a point north of the North Pole is determinable. It is outside the earth itself, in space.

If we assume the existence of God, then all "true" physics falls logically into place; there is less meaninglessness. The Bible says: "The host of heaven cannot be numbered" (Jeremiah 33:22). It invites us to lift up our eyes and look to the heavens and ask, "Who created these?" The answer cannot be contained within the finite earth, because the heavens is unmeasurably vast, and therefore cannot be ignored.

In the minds of Christian scientists, God is the originator of the universe. He existed before the universe was. His claims do not conflict with the observations of science. He claims responsibility for the creation of matter, and everything in heaven and on earth. No other intelligent source does!

1.9   THE STRUCTURE OF THE EARTH

The earth is not round, as the following measurements show. An imaginary straight line connecting the North and the South Poles measures 12,719km, while the equatorial diameter is 12,756km. The circumference at the equator measures 40,076km (It would take some 25 million people holding hands to encircle it!) Scientists have used wavelengths and frequencies from seismology to deduce the nature of the material shock waves have passed through. This technique is used to detect oil, coal and mineral deposits underground and to determine the number of layers which compose the earth's structure. The earth is made up of rock and has four main layers: the crust, mantle, outer core and inner core (see Fig. 1.1).

1.9.1 THE CRUST. If the earth were a grapefruit, its crust would be thinner than the peel. However, the thickness of the crust varies between 6 and 40 kilometres. It is on this outer layer that we live.

Scientists tell us that the earth's crust is younger than the other layers, that it forms the granitic rocks of the continents and is made up largely of

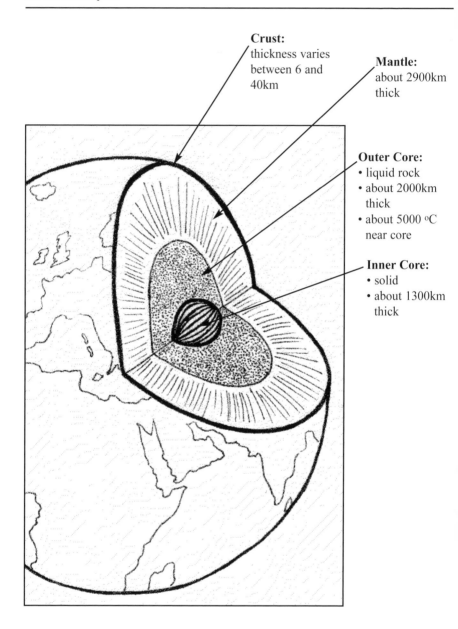

Crust:
thickness varies between 6 and 40km

Mantle:
about 2900km thick

Outer Core:
• liquid rock
• about 2000km thick
• about 5000 ºC near core

Inner Core:
• solid
• about 1300km thick

Figure 1.1: A simplified structure of the earth

oxygen, aluminium and silica. These elements apparently are the scum from the underlying molten surface of the mantle.

The notion of a younger crust can find support from Scripture. Genesis says, God created the earth which was void, empty and formless (Genesis 1:2). The activities of Creation week came after the physical earth came into existence. That is, at some time after the earth was created, it was developed for the habitation of humankind. On day three of that developmental week, God created the dry land – the crust if you like (Genesis 1:9, 10). So the view of a younger outer layer of the earth's structure can be shown to accord with the Genesis account.

1.9.2 THE MANTLE. The mantle is the first layer below the crust. It is about 2000km thick and is so hot that some of its rock is partially melted. It is believed to consist mostly of silicates, and minerals rich in silicon, oxygen, magnesium and iron. The exact composition of the mantle is uncertain, as direct observation is not possible. Seismic study shows that borders of the mantle are solid, with varying degrees of molten rock between them.

1.9.3 THE CORE. Below the mantle is the outer core of liquid rock, about 2000km thick, with temperatures up to 5000°C. The inner, solid core is about 1300km thick. Both the outer and the inner core are believed to consist mainly of iron and nickel.

1.10   THE EARTH IS CONDUCIVE TO LIFE

It is interesting to note that the earth's crust is relatively thin, compared with that of the other solar planets. A thick crust would prevent the heat generated inside escaping quickly and therefore would melt. If the crust were thick, it would also be too rigid and would simply float on top of the mantle. There would be no volcanic eruptions, no mountains, no valleys, and no life. Was it by accident that a thin crust was formed?

The section of the solar system which is more supportive of life is called the ecosphere. Any planet residing in this shell around the sun would not be too cold nor too hot to sustain life forms. The earth is the only planet found inside the ecosphere. Only the earth has life on it. This positioning of the earth is unique, not too near and not too far from the sun. Is this another accident or a coincidence?

Water can be found everywhere in the universe, but it exists mostly as vapour or frozen ice. For instance, the water on Mars is trapped at the frozen poles. In November 1996, Nozette[5] reported in *Science*, that the interpretation of data from a spacecraft suggested the possibility of ice on the surface of the Moon. Most of the Moon's surface is exposed to a temperature of about 122°C. Any ice exposed to such heat would soon evaporate. The ice, however, is believed to be situated in the bottom of a permanently shadowed crater, near the Moon's south pole. Here on earth, seven-eighths of the surface is covered mostly by water. The temperature varies between 60°C and -90°C. The range of temperature together with liquid water makes it ideal for the development and sustenance of life on earth. These conditions – thin crust, ideal distance from the sun, good range of temperatures, just the right size to maintain its atmosphere, and liquid water with its unusual properties (eg. high latent heat of evaporation and fusion, hydrogen bonding, high surface tension) – make the earth an ideal place for life among the planets. Furthermore, the conditions are right for the comfort of humankind. The other planets with their extremes of temperatures, thick crust, etc. do not sustain human forms or any discernible living organisms. There are no scientific reasons put forward to explain why only the earth has all the right conditions to support life in our solar system.

The probability of an accident producing these favourable conditions is nil. What then is a viable alternative to the theories already expounded?

1.11   GOD IS THE ALTERNATIVE

Christians believe that God created the heavens and the earth. Genuine belief is not a thoughtless mental activity. It is the logical outcome of serious investigation into the subject. We cannot therefore believe in the God of the Bible unless we seriously investigate that God which the Bible reveals. Neither can we legitimately deny the claims of the Bible, before we have given careful consideration to its teachings. To do otherwise would implicate us in deception.

A careful reading of Genesis chapter 1 will leave us thinking: Well, it is clear that an intelligent Being, God, did some marvellous things. His work is logical: creating Earth (with its various layers and water surrounding it), light, atmosphere, green plants, the day/night sequence, birds, animals and humans. Looking more closely, we see a number of connecting steps: light and green plants produce oxygen for the animals and humans and the sustenance of the atmosphere; trees supply food and shelter for the birds; work precedes rest. Good. But while the power of this intelligent Being shines through His creative work, "In the beginning God created the heavens and the earth" does not adequately reveal God to us. In a way, Genesis 1 conceals God from us. It tells us about His mighty power but that is not enough to establish our "belief" in Him!

Before we can believe absolutely that God created the heavens and the earth, we need to place the Genesis Creation account within the wider context of the Bible; we need to appreciate God's character, His track record and His supernatural attributes that are evident in the Scripture. On the human level, it is unwise to trust someone on the basis of one good deed, or a fascinating feat that that person has performed. Mutual trust between two individuals develops over time, as the good attributes of both individuals are authenticated.

The Bible itself encourages us to seek and to verify that something is true before we accept it. This provides a kind of scientific method for substantiating a truth or a fact. It says "…[we] must enquire, probe and investigate it thoroughly. And if it is true…" then, accept it. (Deuteronomy 13:12–14). Some of us may have doubts about the authority of the Bible. The God of the Bible says that the messages found in it are not those of human beings. God Himself inspired men to write His messages (2 Timothy 3:16). Also, if we get to know the Bible, we will come to agree that "God is truthful" (John 3:33).

Truth is factual. If God is holy, reliable and truthful, and if the Bible is the Word of God, then we must "enquire, probe and investigate it thoroughly" in order to establish the character of God before we can confidently believe in Him. But, what is there to investigate? Well, if all the claims in the Bible about God are true, then it is only reasonable to expect Him to have left tangible evidences for any investigator who wishes to validate His character, authority and authenticity.

One writer confidently says: "God never asks us to believe without giving sufficient evidence upon which to base our faith … those who really desire to know truth will find plenty of evidence on which to rest their faith".[6]

What are some of the faith-building evidences found in the Bible? In Genesis we have the Creation account, which demonstrates God's power. It gives details of the origin of the universe. It explains the origins of seasons and time. There are real benefits to be obtained from resting after a week's work, and worshipping a supreme Being (Genesis 2). We also will find details of a universal Flood which left vast deposits of fossilised animals and plants (Genesis 6). There we also discover the origins of nations and languages (Genesis 10, 11). Psychologists are still baffled over the development and the origin of speech! Dr. J. G. Penner, citing thirty-two authorities on the origin of language and speech, comments, "Linguists, anthropologists, archaeologists, psychologists, biologists, philosophers, educators and other scholars are compelled to admit ignorance concerning the origin and development of language and speech in prehistoric times."[7] The Bible is quite clear, however, about how nations and languages came about.

The detail and the accuracy of the Bible – confirmed by secular historians and archaeologists – declare one thing: The Author of the Bible is a supreme Being who is worthy to be worshipped. He says of Himself. "I am God, and there is none else; I am God and there is none like me; declaring the end from the beginning, and from ancient times things that are not yet done" (Isaiah 46:9, 10).

In the midst of all this, the Bible says of God: "He spreads out the northern skies over empty space; he suspends the earth over nothing." (Job 26:7). And God himself looks at humankind's quest to find a theory of origin and asks: "Where were you when I laid the earth's foundation? Tell me if you understand." (Job 38:4)

References:

1. Lederman, Leon. *The God Particle* (Bantam Press, London, 1993).
2. Lerner, Eric J. *The Big Bang Never Happened.* (Simon and Schuster, London, 1991).
3. Gould, S J. *An Urchin in the Storm.* (Norton, London, 1987).
4. Hawkins, Stephen W. *A Brief History of Time.* (Guild Publishing, London, 1989)
5. Nozette et al., *Science*, v274, p1495, 1996.
6. White, E G. *Steps to Christ.* (Pacific Press Publishing Association), 105.
7. Penner, J. G. *Evolution Challenged by Language and Speech.* (Minerva Press, London, 2000)

2

CLIMBING UP AND DOWN THROUGH THE GEOLOGIC COLUMN

2.1 THE GEOLOGIC COLUMN: WHAT IS IT?

When we look at the rock layers throughout the world, there is no special "column" that we can point to as the geologic column. The geologic column is more like a map – it is a representation of something real. There is nowhere on the earth, however, where the full geological column can be viewed. It is therefore more complex than a map, because it is usually based on information from widely different areas. Geology is the study of rocks and also the fossils they contain. It has many features which help us to visualise or understand what we are talking about. One of these is the geologic column, which is a representation of the order in which the rock layers are laid down in the earth. The various layers of rock that we see over Earth's surface, can sometimes be compared to the layers of a wedding cake that lie neatly one above the other. One can think of the geologic column as a slice through all the tiers of the cake. The slice gives the order and type of all the layers. Similarly, the geologic column is a representation of the order of the layers of rock we find on Earth's surface, together with the type of each layer.

The picture is complicated or even confused by the fact that in many places, parts of the geologic column are missing. For instance, we can follow two rock layers for great distances, with one lying just on top of the other. But a little farther we may find a third layer with different kinds of fossils, or a different rock type appears between the first two layers. This third layer, which was missing in one locality, has to be added to complete the geologic column. In some places, many of the layers of the geologic column and their fossils are well represented. In other places only a few layers are present. However, there are notable similarities in the layers over much of Earth, and many facts concerning the geologic column apply generally to many places.

One of the places where we can get a good look at some of the layers of the geologic column, is the Grand Canyon of the Colorado River in Arizona, USA (Figure 2.1). Here, over a kilometre of layers has been exposed by extreme erosion. In the Grand Canyon, the upper part of the general geologic column is missing, and only parts of the lower portion are present. Some of these missing parts are found elsewhere on Earth. The portions of the geologic column that are found in the Grand Canyon are much thicker than usual. The complete, detailed geologic column is not found in any one place.

2.2   HOW WAS THE GEOLOGIC COLUMN PUT TOGETHER?

For years, scientists studied rocks and the fossils they contained from all over the world. They noted that fossil dinosaurs were found below horses, and that both were above crab-like animals called trilobites, which, like dinosaurs, no longer live on Earth. Many more details were discovered. It was also noted that below a certain level, the rocks had hardly any fossils at all. If there were any, they tended to be very small, usually composed of only one cell. These lower rock layers with no fossils or a few small ones are called Precambrian. By combining rock types from many localities, scientists have assembled a general geologic column, to represent the order of the fossils and rocks found over Earth. Figure 2.2 gives a simplified version of the geologic column showing the main divisions. The lowest layer was formed first and the top layer last.

2.3   HOW RELIABLE IS THE GEOLOGIC COLUMN?

Sometimes the question is raised about the dependability of the geologic column. Can we trust a sequence that has been put together from various parts of Earth? There is no question that some small parts of the geologic column have been put together on the basis of rather poor information, and there is no doubt that there will be a number of minor revisions in the column, over time. On the other hand, the general arrangement of the geologic column has been found to be consistent with the evolutionary criteria used to put it together.

When we find certain characteristic fossils, we can usually predict which kinds of fossils will be found below and above that layer. From time to time, fossils are found out of place in the column. This usually leads to revisions of the details of the column. Also, in a few places, significant sections of the geologic column appear out of order. We shall discuss these a little later. In order to understand the significance of all this, we must first consider the relation of the geologic column to the biblical concept of Creation and to the theory of evolution.

Figure: 2.1: A view of the geologic column. Grand Canyon Arizona, U.S.A

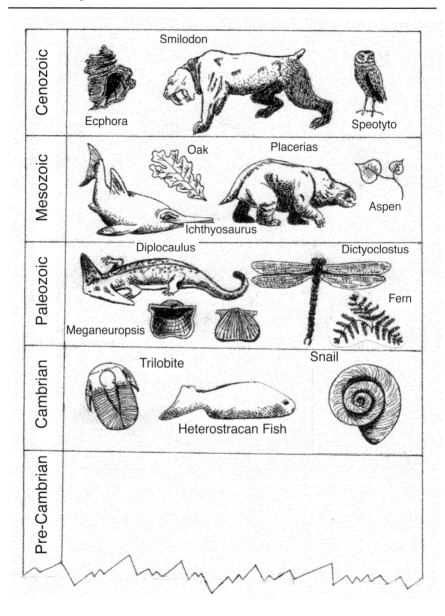

Figure 2.2: A simplified version of the geologic column

2.4   A GREAT QUESTION: WHICH IS TRUE – EVOLUTION OR CREATION?

Most scientists support the general theory of evolution. This is the idea that life on Earth started by itself and over many millions of years the early, simple life-forms gradually changed into more and more advanced organisms, which eventually produced man. This idea presents many problems, one being the fact that no good way of starting life and causing it to develop completely into an advanced form by itself has been discovered. On the other hand, some scientists believe in Creation. This is the fact that the various kinds of living organisms were created by God a few thousand years ago, as described in the Bible. The Bible also describes a great worldwide Flood which took place many years after Creation. This Flood could have been responsible for much of the geologic column.

One very significant difference between Creation and evolution is that Creation proposes that most of the general geologic column was laid down quite rapidly during the year of the biblical Flood, while evolutionists present that the column was laid down over billions of years. The question of whether evolution or Creation is correct is important, because the answer affects our belief in the Bible, which is God's Word. If we believe in the Bible, the question cannot be easily ignored. Many have struggled over the rightness or wrongness of the theory of evolution and Creation. Many more will struggle.

2.5   EVOLUTION AND THE GEOLOGIC COLUMN

As we look at the geologic column, it appears that organisms get generally more complex as we go from bottom to top (Figure 2.2). Simple life is present in the lowest "Precambrian" layers. Just above this are more complex marine animals in the lower part of the Palaeozoic layers. Just above these, in the upper Palaeozoic and Mesozoic layers are more advanced terrestrial organisms; while in the uppermost Cenozoic layers we find mostly mammals and flowering plants, which are considered to be the most advanced organisms on Earth. In general, simpler organisms are also found in the upper layers, while the more advanced organisms are not found in the lower layers.

The general trend towards some increased complexity, as one goes up the geologic column, is probably the strongest evidence there is for evolution. Evolutionists believe that the fossils of simple life, found in the lower rocks of the geologic column, represent some of the first forms of life that evolved some three-and-a-half-billion years ago. Most other organisms evolved much later, starting about half-a-billion years ago at the beginning of the Palaeozoic part of the geologic column. Evolution is thought to have proceeded over hundreds of millions of years, and the various new kinds of organisms became buried and formed fossils as the geologic column was slowly laid down.

2.6 AN EARLY CREATIONIST INTERPRETATION OF THE GEOLOGIC COLUMN: MOVING AROUND IN CIRCLES.

Early in the 20th century, some creationists who believed that life came as a result of the recent Creation by God, and not as the result of evolution over billions of years, started to focus on the geologic column. They began to wonder if there really was a general order to the fossils in the geologic column, and, if so, whether the more complex organisms were really near the top. They noted that in several places over the world the fossils were out of the expected order. For instance, in Switzerland, around the famous Matterhorn peak, lower Palaeozoic layers were found above the higher Mesozoic layers. This is contrary to the normal arrangement in the geologic column. In the northern United States, in Glacier Park, a huge section of Precambrian layers lies above the Mesozoic ones (see Figure 2.2 for the order of the geologic column). Evolutionists had interpreted these Mesozoic layers to be 900 million years younger than their position suggests. It is these anomalies that are used to suggest that the order in the geologic column is not reliable. But there was no compromise as to the allotted age of each layer. The fossils were the key to their age. It was already assumed that each rock level would contain a certain type of fossil. So wherever that fossil was found, the layer was given that age. So one could argue that the layer dates the fossil and the fossil dates the layer. Suggestions were made that the evolutionists were moving around in circles – using the fossils to date the rocks, regardless of their position in the geologic column. This system was bound to work. It is called circular reasoning. But is it scientific?

This argument against the geologic column was pursued for decades by some who believe in Creation. However, this discrepancy no longer seems to be a strong point for Creation. The reason is, it has been found that in most places over Earth the general order of the geologic column seems reliable. The few places where it is not in order, such as the examples in Switzerland

and the United States, mentioned above, seem to be places where lower (older) layers have been pushed up and then pushed horizontally over layers that were originally higher (younger). While the argument of evolutionists moving around in circles seems to be invalid and the geologic column seems to have some credibility, creationists do have other explanations for the geologic column, which we shall now consider.

2.7 A MORE RECENT CREATIONIST INTERPRETATION OF THE GEOLOGIC COLUMN: THE ECOLOGICAL ZONATION THEORY

The Flood is one of the most dramatic events described in the Bible. It was a world-wide event. The reason for this Flood was that man had become so evil that God had to cleanse Earth, and He did it with water.

Heavy rainfalls do cause some erosion of the soil on the surface of the land. The water from the rain carries this soil into streams and rivers and eventually into lakes and oceans. The soil consists mainly of fine particles of clay, silt, and sand. These particles are called sediment. Over a long time, sediments become cemented into soft or hard rocks called sedimentary rocks. These rocks often contain a few fossils. It turns out that most of our geologic column consists of sedimentary rocks, and creationists believe that most of the geologic column was formed from sediment carried by the waters of the Flood described in the Bible. The Flood waters brought sediments and organisms together to form the fossil-bearing rock layers of the geologic column.

An important question is: How could a flood cause organisms to be ordered in the increasing complexity we observe in the geologic column? One answer proposed by creationists is based on the fact that on Earth we find a general increase in complexity of living organisms, as we go from lower to higher regions.

It is argued that as the surface of Earth was broken up and the Flood waters gradually rose, the big waves eroded the various regions (hills, valleys, plains, etc.). The simpler organisms lower down were buried first and the more complex ones later, thus producing, as we go up the geologic column, a sequence from simpler to more complex.

At present on the surface of Earth, we have many simple microscopic organisms that live in the rocks, sometimes kilometres down. Above them we have complex marine animals living in the oceans, and higher up still we find more complex terrestrial forms of life. We do notice this same general sequence in the geologic column. There we have simple organisms in the Precambrian, moderately complex marine organisms in the lower part of the Palaeozoic, and more complex terrestrial organisms above in the upper Palaeozoic, Mesozoic, and Cenozoic. The idea that the general distribution pattern, or ecology of Earth before the Flood is responsible for the sequence of fossils that we find in the geologic column, is called the "ecological zonation theory".

2.8 QUESTIONS ABOUT ECOLOGICAL ZONATION

In a number of ways, the present ecological distribution of organisms on Earth fits in well with the geologic column, but there are some notable exceptions. For instance, in the geologic column we find flowering plants and mammals mainly in the Cenozoic; this would have been high up in the terrestrial region before the Flood, as proposed by the ecological zonation theory, while on Earth we now find these kinds of organisms way down to seashore level. This can be accounted for by proposing some differences in the ecological distribution of organisms before the Flood, compared to the present distribution. For instance, it could well be that before the Flood, mammals and flowering plants did not live in the lower terrestrial regions. Other organisms that lived there, such as dinosaurs and many of the coal-producing plants that are now extinct, were better adapted and thrived there.

It has also been proposed that before the Flood there were seas at different levels. This could explain the presence of some marine organisms high in the geologic column. Figure 2.3 is a suggestion of how organisms might have been distributed on the landscapes of Earth before the great Flood of the Bible. One should also note that the sequence of organisms in Figures 2.2 and 2.3 is similar. That is, the landscapes of Figure 2.3 fit the geologic column of Figure 2.2. However, we should not expect an exact agreement between the ecological distribution of plants and animals before the Flood and the present geologic column. Movements of both land and water during the Flood could produce different arrangements of sediments and organisms which eventually formed fossils. Also, one should not expect that the ecological distribution of organisms on the earth before the Flood would

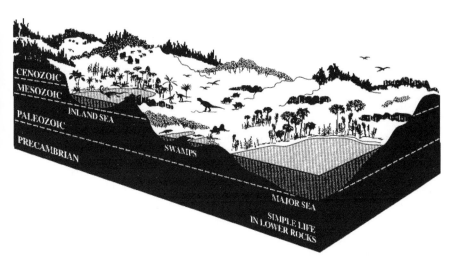

Figure 2.3: Proposed preflood landscape.

match present distribution patterns. A world-wide Flood would most likely have significant effects on the ecological distribution of organisms on Earth. This would produce differences in the distribution of organisms before and after the Flood. Hence, as an explanation for the order of the fossils in the geologic column, present ecological distribution should be expected to provide only general agreement with the geologic column.

2.9 EVIDENCE THAT SUPPORTS ECOLOGICAL ZONATION

We have already pointed out that there is somewhat of a general increase from simple to complex in living organisms, as we go from lower to higher regions of Earth's crust. We find microscopic organisms in the deep rocks, more complex organisms in the oceans above these deep rocks, and the most complex organisms on the higher land above the oceans. If this sequence were destroyed by the Flood, we would expect it to be reflected in the geologic column – and it is. Simple organisms would already be in the deep rocks before the Flood. The marine organisms would be buried as the "fountains of the deep were broken up," as mentioned in the biblical Flood account, and the landscapes above the deep would be gradually destroyed by the mighty force of the rising water.

Another piece of evidence that is explained by ecological zonation is the fact that, as we go up the geologic column, we suddenly encounter all kinds of marine animals at the base of the Palaeozoic. These would represent the sediment and organisms of the seas before the Flood. This sudden appearance of marine animals is what we would expect from a Flood, and not what would be expected from a slow process of gradual evolution.

We do not find any significant representation of terrestrial (land) organisms, in the lower part of the Palaeozoic. However, at about the middle of the Palaeozoic a great variety of terrestrial organisms appears, such as fungi, mosses, horsetails, ferns, insects, centipedes, millipedes, spiders and amphibians. The appearance of so many terrestrial organisms at this point in the geologic column would represent the destruction, by the Flood, of the lowest dry land regions. These lower lands would have had many different kinds of terrestrial habitats. An important question that needs answering by the supporter of the slow evolutionary process is, "Why should so many different kinds of terrestrial organisms evolve at about the same place in the geologic column?"

2.10   OTHER EXPLANATIONS FOR THE INCREASE IN COMPLEXITY OF ORGANISMS IN THE GEOLOGIC COLUMN

As we go up the geologic column, we find that the amphibians start before reptiles, and reptiles start before birds and mammals. Evolutionists interpret this as gradual evolutionary advancement over long periods of time. On the other hand, experiments have shown that when the dead bodies of these different kinds of animals are placed in water, as would have happened during the Flood, at first they all float, then after about one week the amphibians sink. A few weeks later the reptiles sink, and the birds and mammals sink after many weeks. In a Flood, the dead bodies would be buried after they sank. These facts fit the sequence of fossils as they appear in the geologic column when a Noachian Flood is considered.

Some animal groups such as dinosaurs and rodents get larger as one goes up through the geologic column. This has been called Cope's rule. Evolutionists interpret this as evolutionary advancement, from smaller to larger sizes. However, we would probably expect the same pattern during the biblical Flood, as larger animals of the same type would be able to travel farther and higher as they sought to escape the rising Flood waters. There are many different ways to explain the facts we find in the geologic column.

2.11   PROBLEMS FOR EVOLUTION IN THE GEOLOGIC COLUMN

The evolution of simple organisms into complex ones is assumed to be a slow and gradual process. It would have taken a long time for one organism to change into a slightly different one, and that one into another different one, and so on. Because of this, we should expect to find fossils of all kinds of intermediates in the evolution of one kind of organism into a different kind, as we go up through the geologic column. However, fossils of the expected intermediate types are conspicuously absent. We find, instead, that new types of organisms appear suddenly without any evolutionary ancestors below them. For instance, bats are supposed to have evolved from some kind of mouse-like animal, yet when we look in the geologic column below where we find bats, there are no intermediates of any kind. The very lowest bat we find in the column is very much like our modern bat, complete with fully developed wings. There are a few rare exceptions where evolutionary ancestors are postulated for mammals and birds (e.g. Archaeopteryx), but evolution would require that every major group has its line of ancestors below it in the geologic column. The column does not provide these links, and the intermediates (or missing links) are notoriously absent between the larger groups of both plants and animals, where we would expect the greatest number. This is a problem for evolution. Modified theories, such as punctuated equilibrium, have been proposed as solutions. But as punctuated equilibrium deals mainly with minor changes and not major groups – the problem remains.

Another problem for evolution is the highly erratic rates of evolution we note in the geologic column. In the evolutionary interpretation of long ages, why does evolution appear, at times, to go so extremely fast and at other times so extremely slow? Furthermore, evolution needs all the time it can find for improbable events to bring about changes. Evolution needs to "sit" as long as it can, waiting for improbable events. The billions of years proposed for evolution to occur are already far too short for these improbable events. The problem is further compounded when the geologic column suggests that major evolutionary changes had to occur very rapidly. For instance, life is assumed to have existed on Earth for about 3.5 billion years, yet for approximately the first 3 billion years of that time we see virtually no evolution. We are still almost exclusively in simple one-cell kinds of organisms at the end of that time. Then suddenly, at the beginning of the Palaeozoic, practically all of our major animal groups appear in what is assumed to be only a few million years. Evolutionists call this the "Cambrian Explosion". How did all the evolutionary changes, needed to produce our basic animal groups, occur so fast?

This is a major problem for evolution, but the facts fit in very well with the location of the low seas before the Flood in the ecological zonation model discussed earlier. As we go up higher in the geologic column, we find that most of the major groups of birds and mammals "evolved" in a few million years. This all seems unusual for an evolutionary process that would require an enormous amount of time. The data seems to fit in better with the Creation/Flood concept presented in the Bible.

2.12   CONCLUSION

The geologic column, which represents the layers of rocks and fossils on the surface of our planet, does show some increase in the complexity of organisms as one goes from bottom to top. This increase is considered as evidence for evolution. However, creationists have alternative explanations, based on factors related to the great Flood described in the Bible. These explanations include ecological zonation, and motility factors. The geologic column poses some serious challenges to evolution, both because of highly erratic rates of evolutionary change and the lack of the intermediate organisms that could be expected from a gradual evolutionary process. The geologic column gives credibility to the Genesis account of beginnings.

3

DID GOD USE PLATE TECTONICS TO CREATE DRY LAND?

When God created the earth, He surrounded the land mass with water. No land was visible, only water. This is the picture inferred from Genesis 1:9. As an extension of this, we can take a simplistic view or a faith jump and develop the picture even further.

Since no dry land was visible at the beginning of Creation week, we can deduce that the mountains present today did not exist. Furthermore, we can assume that the solid rock beneath the water was more spherical and even all the way around the globe. There would be no need for great depths. Everett Peterson suggests an average depth of water surrounding Earth to be 610m[1]. We now know that Earth is made up of about twelve curved plates, which include all of the crust and the upper part of the mantle. We also know that these plates move relative to one another and are continuously in motion. Did God use these physical characteristics to create dry land?

Imagine that Earth's crust under water was intact – no separation into separate pieces of land. Say, it was more like the skin on an orange. For God to form dry land, He could have caused the skin to fracture in places to facilitate uplifts. As the land emerged out of the water, the plates would slide over each other, causing the fractures to widen and create submerged trenches as they did so. The water would rush into the trenches revealing more dry land and creating deeper seas.

The movement of Earth's plates relative to one another is called plate tectonics. God could have used plate tectonics to create dry land, on the third day of Creation week. In the process, deep gorges (trenches) would have been created at the fractures or fissures. These would have deepened and widened as more and more crust materials moved into the uplift to form land above the water. It is highly probable that there would have been uplifts (ridges) that did not emerge out of the water. It is not being postulated here that the present physical features of Earth originated entirely during Creation week. The Flood certainly did alter things somewhat. Genesis 7:11 says "all the springs of the great deep burst forth…" It would be more accurate to say that Earth, as we see it today, is the result of our "faith" mechanism of Creation week, substantially modified by the Flood and natural erosion since then.

If we accept this "faith" mechanism for the formation of dry land, the common view that the oceans consisted largely of sunken portions of continents, like the legendary Atlantis or bits of island like Port Royal in Jamaica, should be reviewed in view of present information. The deepest sea is the Pacific Ocean with depths of 10km, a far greater depth than the estimated 610m that existed before Creation week. Mount Everest is the largest visible mountain above sea level, but the Atlantic Ocean has the planet's largest mountain range, some 19,312km long. The formation of these massive uplifts is now credited to the activity surrounding the boundaries where Earth's plates meet. Let's take a scientific overview of this fascinating phenomenon, plate tectonics, which is also contributing to a unifying scientific theory towards the understanding of a variety of Earth's phenomena: earthquakes, volcanoes, etc.

3.1 THE PATH TO PLATE TECTONICS

Earthquakes, volcanoes and mountains have played major roles in human history. Two natural questions to ask are, where did the mountains come from and what causes volcanoes and earthquakes? Questions such as these were asked as far back as the time of the Greek philosophers. With the exploration of the world and the production of accurate maps, questions concerning the relationships of the various shapes of the continents were asked as early as the 1600's. However, it was not until the beginning of the 20th century that realistic answers began to develop. Modern science still does not have a complete understanding of these dynamic Earth processes!

In 1912, Alfred Wegener, a German meteorologist and geophysicist, proposed that the continents of our modern world were once fitted together in a supercontinent called Pangea. Pangea in Greek means "all the land". Wegener believed that sometime in Earth's past history, the supercontinent broke up and the pieces drifted to their present position over a long period of time. This hypothesis was rejected by the scientific community, and anybody who supported it was openly scorned. This is often the case with new and revolutionary ideas. However, over the ensuing years more and more evidence, which could be interpreted as positive support for this theory of "Continental Drift", was obtained through scientific investigation.

In addition to the elegant jigsaw fit of the continents, Wegener's data included the observation of unique fossil and mineral deposits found on the east coast of South America and the west coast of Africa. He reasoned that if the continents were together in the past, then these deposits could be explained as a single deposit, rather than as two unique deposits which just happened to match up. Because Wegener could not answer the "how questions", his hypothesis was rejected.

In the late 1940's, exploration of the ocean floors of Earth began to reveal a wealth of new information, hitherto unobserved. Extremely deep and narrow areas of ocean floor were found and called "trenches". These trenches are observed along most of the borders of the Pacific Ocean. In addition to trenches, underwater mountain ranges were found on the ocean floors. These mountain ranges are called ridges. The most notable is the Mid-Atlantic Ridge which dissects the Atlantic Ocean and extends the length of it. About 1962, the relationship of the trenches and ridges was combined into a theory called Sea-floor Spreading.

Another physical phenomenon, also under investigation in the late 1950's and early 1960's, was evidence of polar reversal of Earth's magnetic field preserved in the rocks of the ocean's floors. In addition to the polar reversals preserved in the rock record, it was observed that there was a mirror-image pattern of these reversals on either side of the ocean ridges. In other words, as the lava spread from these ridges, the magnetic characteristics of the lava were frozen in the sea floor, thereby preserving the direction of Earth's magnetic poles. Magnetic reversal data was also found in terrestrial rocks. However, the sea-floor observations would prove to be the most important data in helping to understand the questions of the dynamics of Earth's crust. It was the magnetic reversal data that substantiated the sea-floor spreading theory.

In the late 1960's, the trenches, ridges, and magnetic reversals of the sea floors were combined with the Pangean fit of the continents to give us the theory of plate tectonics. With this new theory came the support for Wegener's insight into moving continents.

Plate tectonics views the surface of the earth as a series of solid interconnecting plates which are in constant motion. There are basically two types of plates: sea floor plates composed of dense basalt and continental plates composed of less dense granite. These plates can slide along each other, or one plate can dive under another, or they can simply collide into or move away from each other (see figure 4.9 on p65). The various motions of the plates are used to explain earthquakes, volcanoes, mountains, and ocean ridges and trenches.

3.2 PLATE TECTONICS IN ACTION

Earthquakes are associated with all types of plate movements. One of the most widely known earthquake areas in North America is the San Andreas Fault in California. Here, two major plates, the Pacific plate on the west and the North American plate on the east, are sliding past each other. Earthquakes in areas such as Mexico, South America and Japan are the result of one plate diving under another plate. This is formally known as a subduction zone, i.e. one plate is subducted under another.

Trenches are also associated with subduction zones. The deep trenches are the result of the floor of the ocean being pulled down as the plate is subducted. Questions that come to mind whenever subduction is considered are, "What happens to the plate that is subducted?" and, "What fills the hole in the ocean floor as the plate is subducted?" These are good questions.

A plot of the volcanoes, both active and inactive, reveals an interesting pattern. Their locations correspond closely with subduction zones and plate boundaries. It is currently accepted that the friction from the subduction of the lower plate, and its melting deep below Earth's surface, heat a spot in the upper plate which can result in the formation of a volcano. The volcano releases pressure from the steam and gases produced from the melting and subduction of the lower plate.

The "hole" created at the other end of the subducted plate is filled with new floor material from a spreading centre. New ocean floor material is produced at these spreading centres from Earth's mantle and lower crust. The most widely known spreading centre is the Mid-Atlantic Ridge, the effect of which is best observed in Iceland.

Major mountain ranges of Earth can be directly associated with the collision of two plates meeting head on. As the plates come together, the edges of the plates crinkle up to form the mountains. Not all mountains are formed in this way. However, major mountain ranges, such as the Andes and the Himalayas, are assumed to be the result of two plates colliding.

There are six major plates that compose the surface of the Earth. They are, the African, American, Pacific, Eurasian, Indian (sometimes called the Australian), and the Antarctic. These are normally recognisable as the continents. The plate boundaries are clearly defined through a plot of Earth's volcanoes, and earthquake epicentres.

What makes the system go? Why do the plates move at all? Why are there plates in the first place? These and other questions are current topics of active research. No-one knows the answers. Only unproven hypotheses based on simple models are offered as answers. One of the more promising models is based on convection currents.

Convection currents can be observed in a pot of near-boiling water. As one carefully observes the surface of the water, it is possible to see areas where hot water is rising, from below, to the surface and other areas where the cooler water is sinking below the surface. These cycles of rising and sinking water are called convection currents. It is possible to have more than one of these currents in the same pot.

Now consider Earth as the pot of water. The lower portions of Earth's mantle are heated and rise towards the surface of Earth, possibly forming a new ocean floor at the spreading centres. The cooler portion of the convection current can be seen as the area of subduction. The surface plates would then move about these convection currents, much like a small particle of dust would move about in the pot of water. This is why it is often said, "The upper crust floats on jelly."

Based upon the current rates of movement, the time factors associated with the theory of plate tectonics run into millions of years. If the plates are moving at the average rate of 5 cm each year, and South America and Africa were once together and are now thousands of kilometres apart, it would take several million years to bring them to their present positions. How do Christians, who believe in a short chronology for the life of this planet, relate to these time frames?

One possible theory for plate tectonics in a short time-frame would be to suggest that before the Genesis Flood the dry land formed Pangea. Towards the end of the Flood, Pangea was broken up into the various continents which were then rapidly moved to their near present positions. The currently measured rates of plate movements were established at the end of the Genesis Flood and are what are observed today.

3.3   CONCLUSION

We must realise that there are problems associated with this explanation, such as where did all of the heat go from moving the plates so rapidly? There is no ready answer. However, there are many missing answers in the standard interpretation (not reproduced here) also! We just don't know, yet. It does seem possible, however, that if a most powerful God created Earth in the first place, He could surely move the continents about Earth's surface with very little trouble.

Reference

1. Peterson, Everett H. *Creation Research Society Quarterly* Vol 18, No. 2, September 1981, p 121.

4

WHY THIS POSITION – ROCK LAYERS IN THE EARTH?

Often, when we drive or walk through countryside, particularly on the coast, we see layers of rock standing on end, twisted, folded and sometimes lying flat (Figure 4.1). It is obvious, even to the casual observer, that something must have caused these layers to move. Two questions come to mind: 1) What makes the layers? and 2) What moved the layers? To answer these questions we shall have to look more closely at the rocks themselves.

4.1 WHAT MAKES THE LAYERS?

There are different types of rocks that form the layers we see in the earth. Some rocks look like mud or dirt and that is just what they are. Geologists call them mudstones (Figure 4.2). If the mudstone breaks in layers instead of in chunks, they call it shale (Figure 4.3). Mudstone and shale are soft rocks that are easily eroded and are frequently found on slopes or mountainsides. [The slopes in Figure 4.1 were formed by mudstones and shales.] The slope may be underlain or capped by harder rocks, such as sandstone or conglomerate.

The names of these rocks tell us a lot about their composition. Sandstone is made of sandy material that has been cemented together by a wide variety of natural "glues" (Figure 4.4). A conglomerate is exactly what it sounds like: a conglomeration or mixture of a wide variety of rounded rock fragments glued together by mud or sand (Figure 4.5). Breccias are similar, but the fragments are angular and sharp cornered.

Another group of rock layers is formed in a very different way. Limestone consists of limey mud and occasionally some fossils. The limey mud and most of the fossil shells are made of calcium carbonate. Many animals that live in the oceans, and in some salt-water lakes, use the calcium and the carbonate molecules from the water to build their shells. An over-abundance of these chemicals in salty waters can combine on their own and settle to the bottom of the sea or lake to form the limey mud. Gypsum and halite (rock salt) may also form in this way or they may form in hot, dry climates as the water in shallow lakes evaporates. Gypsum, halite and other similar rocks are often referred to as "evaporites". All of these kinds of layers are called sedimentary rocks, because they are formed from sediments or loose dirt that has been compressed and/or cemented into rocks.[1]

Where did all the loose dirt come from? Some of the sediments were weathered and eroded from very hard rocks called igneous rocks. Two very common igneous rocks are granite and basalt (Figure 4.6). These rocks are formed when hot, molten material cools and crystallizes. The crystals interlock like a jigsaw puzzle.

At one time, scientists thought that granite had large crystals because it had cooled very slowly below the surface of the earth. Rhyolite has the same crystals in it as granite, but the crystals are microscopic. Since rhyolite frequently occurs as a red- or grey-coloured lava (molten rock that erupts from a volcano), it is assumed that it has microscopic crystals, because it cools quickly on or near the surface. Another factor controlling the size of the crystals is the amount of water present as the molten rock cools.[2] Apparently, some granite forms from molten rock that contains very little water, and rhyolite forms when the melted material contains a lot of water.

Similar processes probably influence the formation of other igneous rocks. Gabbro is a very dark rock with large crystals that are easily seen. Basalt (a black lava) is made of the same crystals as gabbro. BUT they are microscopic. Rocks that are intermediate between the light-coloured granites and the dark-coloured gabbros are called diorites. Diorite has a combination of light and dark-coloured crystals that make it look a little like salt and pepper. Andesite is made of the same crystals as diorite but the crystals are smaller. The small crystals of black "pepper" in andesite make it look grey. The crystal structures of all of these rocks are broken by the action of rain, frost, and wind. Plants send their roots down into structures. The loose material is moved to lower ground by gravity, snow slides, wind and water to a lake or sea where new sedimentary rocks may be formed (Figure 4.7). As igneous and sedimentary rocks get buried, the increased pressures and temperatures deep within the earth cause the rocks to change into a third general category: metamorphic rocks. Limestone becomes marble in these conditions. Shale becomes slate; sandstone changes to quartzite; and granite re-forms into a gneiss.

Of course, there are many more kinds of rocks but all are a part of these three major groups: igneous, sedimentary and metamorphic. These rocks form the layers of the continents on which we live.[3]

4.2   WHAT MOVED THE LAYERS?

How do the layers of rocks get tilted, folded and twisted? There are several ways to change the position of the rocks. Sedimentary rocks may slump downhill, causing the layers to bend, fold and even break (Figure 4.8). This can happen over very large distances, especially when the slump occurs underwater, as in a lake or in the ocean. Such contorted structures are fairly common in sedimentary layers.

Other processes that affect the shape and position of rocks are regional forces of tension (stretching) and compression (squeezing). Scientists believe these forces are caused by the movement of the ocean floor along the edges where the continents meet, such as the mid-Atlantic ridge. As rocks are pulled apart (tension), layers may slip and tilt. The rocks may fracture or break and sometimes there is movement along the fracture. When movement occurs, the fracture is called a fault. If the block of rock above the fracture falls, the fault is called a normal fault or a gravity fault, because the rock moved in the direction of gravity (Figure 4.9b). If the rocks are compressed, the block of rock above the fracture may move up against the force of gravity.

When this happens, the structure is called a reverse or thrust fault (Figure 4.9c). Sometimes the pressure is at an angle to the fracture and the rocks move laterally to form a strike-slip fault (Figure 4.9d). This kind of movement occurs along numerous faults in Southern California, USA (Figure 4.9), and the Great Glen Fault in Scotland.

Faulting causes much of the uplift and exposure of the layers of rocks in mountainous regions. Huge areas of the earth have been deformed by these processes (Figure 4.10). Many people believe that these processes have occurred quite naturally for millions of years. However, those who live in areas with active earthquakes, know that the earth can shift and move several feet in just seconds. If the frequency and intensity of earthquake activity were increased as a result of some catastrophe, mountains could be uplifted within a very short period of time. Such movement may not be as unreasonable as it sounds. The Heart Mountain Gravity Slide in Wyoming (USA) resulted from an earthquake that broke off part of the Bear Tooth Mountain Range. Heart Mountain slid across almost level ground for a distance of 50km (30 miles). Pieces of the mountain broke off and were left behind. Such a catastrophe would most likely have occurred within a few minutes.

The Bible teaches that a catastrophe on a larger scale struck our earth and lasted for more than a year.

Figure 4.1: Layers of rock in the Grand Canyon, Arizona, USA, from the north rim above Phantom Ranch. (Photo courtesy Anne Brennen).

Figure 4.2: Mudstones look like "lumpy mud" that has lost all of its water to become a rock.

Figure 4.3: Shale typically breaks to form flat layers visible as thin, horizontal lines in this photo.

Figure 4.4: The internal structure of sand dunes forms the lines in this sandstone.

Figure 4.5: The rounded pebbles and cobbles in this photo are typical of a conglomerate.

Figure 4.6: Cooled lava flows from cliffs of basalt

Figure 4.7: Loose rocks fall to the base of the cliff to form a talus.

Figure 4.8: These sand layers must have been in a near plastic phase when slumping, and pressure produced the folds seen in this sandstone block

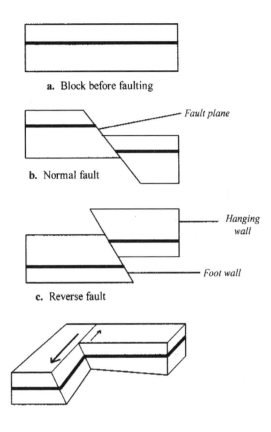

Figure 4.9: Block diagrams of normal, reverse and strike-slip faults

Figure 4.10: Fracturing of the earth's crust can be seen near a road after the June 28, 1992, earthquake near Landers, California, USA The earthquake's reported magnitude was 7.5 on the Richter Scale

In Genesis 6 to 8, the Bible records a catastrophic destruction of our earth. The event is commonly referred to as Noah's Flood. It was not really Noah's Flood; he was in the Ark! Genesis 7:11 records the break-up of the earth's crust. Such global seismic activity must have continued throughout the year of the Flood. (Some suggest that our earthquake activity today is a distant echo of that event.) Is it possible that the ridge-rift system that circles our globe is evidence of that catastrophe? The shattering of the earth's crust is consistent with events recorded in Genesis about the Flood. In addition, a significant amount of the tilted, twisted and interlocking layers could be a direct result of the Flood.

According to the Bible, the Flood destroyed the whole earth, along with most of the marine and freshwater plants and animals. Of the land-dwelling creatures, only those land animals that were in the ark survived. As this event was so devastating, shouldn't there be evidence for Noah's Flood in the visible rock layers of the earth's crust, especially on the continents?

4.3 DO THE ROCK LAYERS SUPPORT A WORLD-WIDE FLOOD?

The continental rock layers have numerous marine deposits. Mountains display graveyards of marine fossils. These widespread marine deposits suggest that portions of the continents were once at the bottom of the sea. These old ocean basins once received tons of marine, freshwater and continental sediments. Today they stand high and dry above sea level. This is where we live. Some scientists do argue that the filling of these old ocean basins required millions of years; that the processes of weathering, erosion and transport of soil and rocks by rivers are responsible for the filling of these basins.[5] However, the extensive marine deposits and the millions of marine organisms they contain could not have been accumulated and preserved by any gradual processes evident today.

In order to preserve the organisms as fossils, the natural recycling process of the marine system has to be stopped.[6] This usually happens in one of two ways: 1) sediment has to cover the organism rapidly and completely to prevent scavengers getting to it, and/or 2) mineralization (flesh becomes impregnated with chemicals such as calcium carbonate) has to occur quickly enough to prevent decay of the soft tissues in some organisms and the disintegration of shells and bones in others. For these conditions to materialise, there must be a massive redistribution of sediment, which would require huge volumes of water, more than anything we observe today. Such conditions could be provided by a world-wide Flood, as described in the Bible.

How did all of this sediment become dry land? As the old ocean filled in, the earth became one large region called Pangea. At some stage Pangea broke apart, forming a new ocean basin (the Atlantic Ocean). During this time, sediments were still being deposited over most of Pangea, which was still largely submerged. As the land mass moved apart and upwards, the ocean basin deepened and the water drained into it, leaving the fragmented Pangea above the sea level as our modern continents. The process would have left a few large inland lakes that eventually dried up, leaving salt deposits like those found in Cheshire, England. Sediment from former lakes and salty deposits are found on continents world-wide, together with extensive deposits of marine fossils on mountains and in the surrounding plains. The mountains would have formed as Pangea broke up, creating the oceans and dry-land masses. The ocean ridges give evidence of the breaking up of Pangea.

How does this picture relate to what the Bible has to say? Genesis graphically portrays what happened to the land masses during the Flood: "… the floodwaters came on the earth … all the springs of the great deep burst forth, and the floodgates of the heavens were opened…. And rain fell on the earth for forty days and forty nights … as the water increased on the earth … all the high mountains under the entire heavens were covered… Everything on dry land that had the breath of life in its nostrils died." (Genesis 7:10–12, 19, 22).

This dramatic description of what took place on our continents does not prove there was a world-wide Flood. However, the observed geological structures and patterns in the layers are what would be expected if there had been such a catastrophe.

The surface of the earth is rugged and uneven, owing to erosion. Gullies and hills are formed as water seeks the path of least resistance to a lake or sea. If loose dirt and soil had been deposited over millions of years, numerous uneven surfaces should have been created. However, the rock layers do not always look uneven. For example, scientists have dated a rock layer to be 225 million years and the rock layer lying just above at 215 million years. If these dates are correct, the time that has passed between the deposition of the two layers is 10 million years. If the surface of that lower layer had been exposed for 10 million years, it would have eroded and appeared uneven. However, these deposits show remarkably little evidence of erosion. Such flat surfaces between deposits extend over hundreds of square kilometres and show little evidence of deposition or erosion.[7] It is reasonable to assume that there is no missing time between the deposition of the two layers. In other words, these planar or flat-lying contacts between the layers cannot represent long periods of time, because there is no evidence of deposition within that 10-million-year gap or erosion of the surface as seen in modern landscapes where rocks are exposed.

4.4 CONCLUSION

Many different kinds of rocks contribute to the layering observed on the earth. These layers are often deformed, tilted and twisted by forces of compression and tension. The critical question is: "Did these forces occur gradually over millions of years or was the Genesis Flood responsible for the upheaval we see as we travel the countryside?" Evidence of a world-wide catastrophe can be found in the rock layers. The continent-wide marine deposits serve as a reminder that our land masses were once ocean floors. The land we walk on today is a record of the large-scale of deposition of sediments that took place in the past. The rock record suggests that large volumes of water were necessary to redistribute these sediments to form our continents. The evidence of smooth surfaces between rock layers, whatever their positions, does not support the millions-of-years concept. Rather, the layers must have formed in quick succession. There are no sources of moving water that simulate the deposition of sediments of this magnitude. No other historical event but the Flood of Genesis could be cited as a cause for such activity.

Some scientists recognise multiple catastrophes in the rock layers but assume that millions of years of time passed between the events. If (as the rock record seems to suggest) the millions of years are not really there, then these multiple catastrophes recorded in the rocks could be attributed to one very complex, world-wide event that lasted for more than a year: the Biblical Flood. (Genesis 8:3–14).

References

1.   Blatt, H., Middleton, G., and Murray, R. *Origin of Sedimentary Rocks*; 2nd ed (Prentice-Hall, Englewood, New Jersey, 1980) 782.

2.   Whitney, J A. *The origin of granite: The role and source of water in the evolution of granitic magmas.* Geological Society of America Bulletin 100:1886–1897 (1988).

3. Press, F. and Siever, R. *Earth*: 4th ed. (W. H Freeman and Company, New York, 1986) 656.

4. Tarbuck, E. J. and Lutgens, F. K. *The Earth*: 2nd ed. (Merrill Publishing Company, Columbus, Ohio, 1987). 590

5. Hauge,T. A. *Kenematic model of a continuous Heart Mountain Allochthon* (Geological Society of America Bulletin, 1990) 102:1174–1188.

6. Malone, D. M. *Evidence of Wapiti Volcanic "Blocks" involved in Heart Mountain Faulting – Implications for the Continuous Allochthon and Tectonic Denudation Models* (American Association of Petroleum Geologists Bulletin, 1992) 76:1263.

7. Nelson, W. H. *Kinematic model of a continuous Heart Mountain Allochthon: Discussion and reply* (Geological Society of America Bulletin, 1991) 103:718–722.

Further Reading:

8. Krumbein, W. C. and Sloss, L. L. *Stratigraphy and Sedimentation*, 2nd Edition (W. H. Freeman and Company, San Francisco, 1963) 660.

9. Donovan, S. K. (ed.) *The Processes of Fossilization* (Columbia University Press, New York, 1991) 303.

10. McCall, P. L. and Tevesz, M.J.S. (eds.) *Animal-Sediment Relations* (Plenum Press, New York, 1982) 336.

11. Beus, S.S. and Morales, M. *Grand Canyon Geology* (Oxford University Press, New York, 1990) 518.

5

COOL RUNNINGS AND THE ICE AGE

Ice, solid water, plays a very important role in our everyday lives. We seldom stop to consider that there was a time in Earth's past when ice also played a very important role. The effects are so long lasting that we have named that time, "The Ice Age". What do we mean when we speak of the Ice Age? What processes were involved? What evidence is there for the Ice Age? When was the Ice Age and how long did it last? These are some of the questions that we shall attempt to explore, and see if the Ice Age fits within our Scriptural world-view.

When we consider the Ice Age, we are investigating a period in Earth's history in which a large portion of the surface was covered by glaciers. In the strictest sense, a glacier is a large body of ice which normally moves down a slope or valley. However, such a definition does not begin to describe the intriguing natural phenomenon known as a glacier, let alone address the Ice Age. So, let us spend some time looking at modern glaciers, see how they are formed, notice how they affect the surface of the earth today, and then look for evidence which supports the concept of the Ice Age in the past.

Glaciers are dynamic entities that currently cover approximately 10% of the earth's land surface (See Table 5.1). They are found on every major land mass except Australia, with the largest concentrations located at the North and South polar regions. While glaciers contain 3% or less of the earth's total water inventory, glaciers contain up to 80% of the earth's fresh water!

An active glacier is composed of two principal parts, an area of accumulation and an area of ablation (melting). The accumulation area is characterized by yearly snowfall exceeding yearly snowmelt, whereas the ablation area is characterized by the yearly snowmelt exceeding the yearly snowfall. Generally, these two areas are separated by the Firn Limit or Annual Snowline. In addition to the snowfall budget (increase and decrease), glaciers are subject to gravity and the environment.

5.1 THE GLACIER BUDGET

The glacier's budget period is seldom of the same length or at the same time every year. A budget period has an accumulation sequence and a melting

Table 5.1: Present -day Ice-Covered Areas (sq. km)

Location	Area Covered
Anatarctica	12, 588, 000
Greenland	1, 802, 600
North-East Canada	153, 000
Central Asia Ranges	115, 000
Spitsbergen Group	58, 000
Soviet Arctic Islands	55, 700
Alaska	51, 500
South American Ranges	26, 500
West Canadian Ranges	24, 900
Iceland	12, 200
Scandinavia	3, 800
Alps	3, 600
Caucasus	1, 800
New Zealand	1, 000
USA (excluding Alaska)	500
Others	100
TOTAL AREA COVERED	**14, 898, 200**

sequence. The beginning of a new budget period is defined as that point where the accumulation of new snow exceeds the melting of the older material. The budget period then extends through the next melting sequence up to the accumulation sequence.

Great forces are at work in maintaining a balanced glacier budget. In times of plenty, the glacier will expand down the valley, and in times of deficit the glacier retreats up the valley in order to maintain a balanced budget. It is very unlikely that within a single year a glacier could be found to achieve stasis. However, over a period of five to ten years balance can be achieved within a small glacier.

The ancestor of the mighty glacier is the delicate, unassuming snowflake. Immediately upon falling to the ground, the snowflake begins to change characteristics. Through the processes of melting, sublimation (from solid directly to vapour), crushing and compaction, thousands of tiny snowflakes are formed into small granules of ice. This initial process takes only a few days or weeks at the most and produces a loose granular aggregate known to skiers as "Corn Snow". This transformation is accompanied by an increase in density from less than 0.10 g/cm^3 to 0.30 g/cm^3 or higher. As the processes of transformation continue, larger, more dense ice crystals are produced. The average glacial ice density is between 0.82 and 0.84 g/cm^3.

Ice that is forming this way cannot be considered a glacier until it begins to move down the slope or valley under its own weight. Internal resistance to flow and external friction forces are seldom overcome until the ice reaches a depth of 18–20m (60–65 feet). In present circumstances the time needed to form this critical depth may take as little as 10 years in places such as Iceland or as long as 100 years in Antarctica.

5.2   GLACIAL FLOW SHAPING THE EARTH

Under ideal conditions, the average speed of glacial flow for a valley glacier averages from 30 to 60cm/day. In very steep areas, this flow rate may exceed 3m/day. Velocities up to 40m/day have been documented for the large outlet glaciers of the Greenland Ice Sheet. Occasionally, short, sudden bursts or surges have been noted for valley glaciers. During a brief advance in 1937, the Black Rapids Glacier in Alaska attained velocities of 75m/day! During that particular surge, the Black Rapids Glacier advanced 4.8km in six months. Today, surges such as the Black Rapid Glacier are the exception rather than the rule.

Once identified, the footprints of past glaciers can be observed in many areas "outside" the current zone of glaciation. Probably the most prominent glacial footprint is the U-shaped valley. Normal erosional processes produce the standard V-shaped valley seen throughout the world. However, as the glacier begins to move down the V-shaped valley, the tremendous forces of the ice carve away the sides and floor of the valley and transform the V-shape into a U-shape. The material thus carved away, is pushed up along the sides and in front of the glacier to form deposits known as moraines.

The formation of glacial moraines can be visualised as being similar, in process, to the drawing of your finger through moist sand. The sand ridges formed along the sides of your finger would be termed lateral moraines and the sand ridge left at the end of your finger would be the terminal moraine. Few valley glaciers have terminal moraines in contact with the ice at present. This is because terminal moraines are formed from advancing glaciers and most of the valley glaciers today are retreating. The lateral moraine is usually most obvious when it leaves the valley sides and swings out onto the plain of the valley, where it forms an arcuate ridge as it merges with the terminal moraine.

Moraines can vary in size and shape, depending upon their age and the activity of the glacier that deposited them. The terminal moraine of the Franz Joseph Glacier, an active glacier in New Zealand, reaches the height of 430 metres. Other high terminal moraines can be found in the northern Italian Alps. Lateral moraines reaching 700–900m in height can be found in the southern French Alps.

Moraines are not always imposing land structures. In North Dakota, USA, there is a series of washboard (ribbed) moraines that reach a height of 1.2 to 4.6m, and are spaced 80 to 170m apart. These washboard features occur at the end of the Mankato drift. Nearly half of the former glaciated area of North Dakota is covered with washboard moraines.

Other prominent glacial footprints include kettle holes, erratics and cirques. A kettle hole is formed when immense chunks of ice are left isolated under layers of drift material as the glacier retreats. As the ice melts, the overlying material slumps down into the void, leaving a kettle-like depression or hole. Often these holes get filled with water and turn into ponds or lakes. Kettle lakes are some of the most dominant features in the northern states of Minnesota and Wisconsin.

The true glacial vagabond is the erratic. Erratics are rocks or boulders that were carried along by the glacier and then abandoned as the glacier retreated. The sizes of erratics vary widely.

One of Europe's best known erratics is the Pierre a Bot or toadstone. This erratic weighs about 3,000 tons and rests in the Jura Mountains of Switzerland, some 112km from its source, Mount Blanc. Erratics can be found throughout Europe and North America. The grand prize for the largest erratic must, however, go to the vast "Schollen" of Germany. The largest erratic there is 4km long, 2km wide, and 120m in thickness!

Regardless of their size or location, erratics give mute testimony to the power and mobility of glaciers.

Other than the U-shaped valley, the glacial cirque is one of the most easily identifiable forms of glacial erosion. In its most classic form, the cirque consists of a rounded basin, partially enclosed by steep cliffs and sometimes containing a small lake or cirque glacier; the cliffs at the back of the basin (head wall) may rise to hundreds or even thousands of metres in height. The cirque is nature's amphitheatre.

Wherever glaciation has occurred or is occurring, cirques will be found. It has been estimated that the Western Cwm (Welsh for cirque – valley) on Mount Everest has a width approaching 4km and a head wall height, with the ice-cap removed, of almost 2,800m (9,200 feet!).

5.3   GLACIATION – A CREATIONIST DILEMMA

There are some Creationists who question the existence of or the argument for an Ice Age because of the estimated time required to develop such extensive glaciation. This position of denial is not desirable, because it ignores so much physical data found throughout the surface of the earth. Until recently, the time estimates for the build-up and melting of the glaciers of the Ice Age were in the tens of thousands of years. One factor for such a long time is that cold air does not carry very much moisture. The moisture is needed to produce the humble little snowflake, which, in turn, produces the mighty glacier.

Many factors are needed to produce the extensive glaciation of the Ice Age. Glaciers are the offspring of climate. They are totally dependent upon the elements of climate for their birth and sustenance. Meteorological factors determine their location, size, activity, and life span. The relationship between glaciers and the controlling factors is seldom simple or straightforward. It is because of these multiple factors that most models for the Ice Age require long periods of time.

In order for glaciers to form, it is necessary to have more than colder winters with high levels of snowfall. Rather than cooler winters playing a key role, it is the cooler summers that are important, coupled with higher levels of winter snowfall. And herein lies the problem: cooler air contains less moisture than warmer air. Because of this problem, some investigators have even invoked collisions with ice asteroids as the possible source for the polar ice caps.

There is significant evidence to support summer cooling effects of volcanic ash within the meteorological records. Following the eruption of Tambora in the Autumn of 1815, the succeeding year, 1816, was known as "the year without a summer". The explosion of Krakatoa in 1883 lowered the mean earth temperature about 1°C for several years.

Evidence for Pleistocene volcanism is abundant world-wide, with at least 68 large ash falls being identified in the western United States alone. With the summer cooling from the volcanic action, only a source of abundant moisture over a sustained period of time would be needed for the beginning of an "Ice Age."

5.4   ICE AGE – PRECIPITATED BY THE FLOOD

Michael J. Oard, a Christian meteorologist employed with the USA National Weather Service, recognised a potential source of sustained moisture in the warm post-Flood waters. After careful, detailed calculations, Oard published a technical monograph entitled, "An Ice Age Caused by The Genesis Flood" in which he outlined all of the major parameters necessary for the development of the Ice Age in a relatively short period of time. Oard calculated that from these simple conditions, the volcanic-induced cooling, coupled with the warm post-Flood oceans would be capable of developing the Pleistocene Ice Age coverage in about 500 years. Assuming a decrease in the amount of volcanism and the lowering of the ocean surface temperatures, Oard felt that his conservative calculations could account for the ablation (melting) of the ice sheets to near current levels in about 700 years. The total Ice Age could occur within 1,500 years, or fewer, instead of tens of thousands of years, the time which is normally reported.

Oard's model does not answer all of the troublesome questions concerning the Pleistocene Ice Age. However, it does go a long way in presenting a viable alternative to a long-age model. The multiple "ice ages" proposed by standard models could be addressed as simple budget balancing of the ice sheets of only one Ice Age. During the ablation of the ice sheets, drainage basins and large stream meandering could be developed in areas that are presently desert. The mixing of cold-tolerant animals with warm-tolerant animals could be explained as migration consequences of the advancing ice sheets.

5.5 CONCLUSION

The extinction of the woolly mammoth has raised some problems for the standard long-ages model, due to these models' severe climatic requirements for glaciation. Even today, the terrain of Alaska and Siberia is not compatible for the support of large herds of such mammals. Therefore, for mammoths and other large mammals to have lived there in vast numbers, the climate had to be milder. The extinction of the mammoth could have been due to the rapid cataclysmic climatic cooling brought on from volcanism as predicted by Oard's model.

The Pleistocene Ice Age glaciation features can be logically and scientifically attributed to a single event. Moreover, a scientifically sound model does exist, which is totally compatible with the Biblical time constraints and the Genesis Flood.[1]

So, where does this put us as Christians? I personally think that we have a position that is neither second class scientifically nor compromising Scripturally. True, we do not have all of the answers, but, neither does anybody else! Whenever the topic of the Ice Age comes up, we do not have to go and stand in the corner because we are embarrassed; in fact, we can join in with confidence, even suggesting possible answers to some of the problems that confront the standard interpretation. We might be surprised at the reactions to a simple question such as, "How differently would things look if the multiple episodes of the Ice Age were really due to the advancement and retreat of a single Ice Age?" What would this bring to the discussion?

Reference

1. Oard, M.J. An Ice-Age Caused by the Genesis Flood. ICR Technical Monograph, Institute for Creation Research, El Cajon, California, 1900

6

MAKING A SEAM OF COAL

6.1 MS DAISY'S COAL IS BEST

When I was a child, the merchants would visit my little district, Cold Spring, in the Parish of St James, Jamaica, to buy "coal". (There was no distinction between the black amorphous material – charcoal – made from burning wood in a deficiency of oxygen, and coal obtained by mining geological coal seams). They would all go directly to Ms Daisy before anybody else. Only when she had sold all her stock would they buy from others. The merchants would say, "Ms Daisy's 'coal' is the best money can buy."

What made Ms Daisy's "coal" better than that of all the other "coal" producers? All of them used the same variety of woods, the same basic procedure and the end products looked the same – black. One Sunday I watched as Ms Daisy prepared to make charcoal.

There was a pile of freshly chopped logs nearby. Ms Daisy instructed her helpers to dig a shallow, crater-like pit in the fine-grained soil, heaping up the removed earth on one side. She constructed a tepee-shaped structure of very dry wood and bramble in the middle of the crater, and carefully packed all the green logs around and above it to form a broad-based cone. To one side was a small opening from which more dry wood and easily burned material were arranged in the form of a wick to the tepee construction.

The helpers set about covering the whole structure with layers of broad leaves, then with green grass and finally with a lot of loose earth. Every effort was made to ensure that every single piece of log was covered several times over and that there was no air vent, except the deliberate opening on the side. The wick was lit, and after the fire was established for about an hour, the small opening, too, was sealed. The mound stood there motionless, in silence, with a solitary observer – Ms Daisy; but within the belly of the mound there was much activity: the process of destructive distillation, where green wood was being heated by hot gases and steam to separate a mixture of volatile substances from the wood. After about three days the mound collapsed, revealing the unburnt black mass of carbon (charcoal) in its belly.

Ms Daisy's "coal" was better because she had a more efficient system. She sealed the mound more carefully, preventing air getting in. This encouraged better circulation of the hot gases inside the mound, which meant the wood became charcoal more from the heat of gases than from any fire heat. Fire heat would have used up some of the carbon in the wood. Ms Daisy's "coal" had a higher carbon content and therefore produced more heat when burned.

6.2   GEOGRAPHICAL DISTRIBUTION OF COAL

Countries within the tropics that do not have opencast coal mines or the means to excavate deep down to retrieve coal reserves, normally produce a limited supply of charcoal for domestic uses, as Ms Daisy did. This source of charcoal does not form part of the statistics of coal reserves; neither is it taken into consideration when dealing with the distribution of coal.

Natural deposits of coal are found on every continent, including Antarctica, and on many islands. A single stratum of coal is known to be continuous over thousands of square kilometres. This kind of distribution and its texture make it easier to estimate world coal reserves than those of oil and gas.

The technique of seismology has been used to estimate the world's reserve of recoverable coal to be about 8 trillion tons. There are trillions of tons of additional coal that is either too deep or the seams are too thin for economical recovery. All the coal used so far amounts to only 1.7% of the minable reserve,[1] leaving a vast amount of fossil fuel for human use.

In some areas, coal is more concentrated than others. For instance, Wales and Staffordshire, in England, have been known to be rich in coal. China is reported to have a reserve of 150 billion tons; Alberta in Canada has 673 billion tons and Nova Scotia alone is purported to have sufficient reserves to provide 100 million tons each year for 15,000 years.[2] That is a lot of coal.

It would appear, then, that the geographical distribution of coal and the amount available makes it still a most valuable fossil fuel that is accessible for a very long time to come. The significance of this becomes more acute when we realise that the world reserves of oil and gas may become exhausted during the next century.[3]

6.3   VALUE AND USES OF COAL

Coal was discovered in America by the early explorers in Illinois in 1673, but it is reported to have been in use in Wales some 4000 years previously. It became an important fuel for heating houses in the 18th century, when major production started. By 1970, some 133 billion tons of coal had been mined. This is only a small fraction of the minable coal. Alberta alone could supply the world with 1 million tons of coal each year for 673,000 years.

The discovery of oil and gas has consistently reduced the amount of coal mined. In 1964, Britain produced 188 million tons of saleable coal. This fell to 99 million tons in 1985 and 31 million tons in 1995. Oil and gas reserves, however, are expected to run out in the next century and coal will once again become the important fossil fuel it has been in the past. Areas such as Lancashire and Yorkshire would have been insignificant counties if it had not been for coal. It was coal that produced the iron to make engines for the railroads which contributed to the nineteenth century industrial revolution in these counties. Subsequently, coal has been used in power stations to produce electricity.

Chemically, the effective reaction of coal is a simple one:

$$Coal + oxygen = carbon\ dioxide + water + heat.$$

All the uses of coal are dependent on how effectively the heat can be harnessed for use.

6.4   WHAT IS COAL?

As illustrated earlier, charcoal can be derived from the destructive distillation of wood. As a matter of fact, both charcoal and coal have the same precursor – green vegetation. If the vegetable matter is not wood, it must first be compacted into an organic muck before it can turn into coal. Coal is the residue of the major component of vegetation, carbon, following the removal of gases. Its wide geographical distribution, particularly in cold regions such as Alaska, Antarctica and Siberia, contributes to the argument that coal is a legacy of the earth, which once had a uniform tropical past. Different areas can produce different types of coal. The type produced is directly related to the carbon content of its precursor. Peat (50% carbon) contains the least amount of carbon; lignite (brown coal) contains 70%. Bituminous coal is the most common and it contains 80% carbon while anthracite is mostly carbon (98%). Coal in its various forms serves as a fuel for both domestic and industrial uses.

6.5 HOW WAS COAL FORMED?

The formation of the trillions of tons of coal deposits is outside human influence. Traditional (evolutionary) data state that land and freshwater plants first evolved some 400 million years ago and that the oldest coal seam dates back 370 million years. If we use the same evolutionary method of assigning age, it is assumed that humans, Homo erectus, came on the scene about 800,000 years ago. This would be some 369 million years after the purported oldest coal seam was formed.

The various ranks of coal (peat, lignite, bituminous and anthracite) were developed mainly by a varying degree of pressure and temperature over time. Firstly, vegetation is compacted (compressed) and buried; and, depending on the amount of pressure from the overlying substance, one type or another rank of coal is formed. More pressure causes the compressed organic muck to be heated internally, and destructive distillation (the removal of gases) results in the formation of coal. The greater the temperature and pressure, the higher the rank of coal produced. Anthracite, the highest rank, depends more on depth (pressure) than on time.

None of the vast coal deposits reveals any gradation in rank on any one site from the bottom up. This does suggest that the partly altered plant remains, which form organic muck, show no signs of progressive transformation into coal.[4] There is normally either peat, lignite, bituminous or anthracite coal, not a mixture of these in any one seam. The largest rank of bituminous coal, however, is sometimes subdivided into high, medium and low volatile substances. This is a measure of how much gas escapes from the organic muck when it is compressed and heated. The lower the volatile content of the coal, the higher its carbon value and the more heat it will produce when burned. There are two basic theories which explain the entire process involved in the formation of coal. The first and traditional evolutionary theory says: plants accumulate in place in large freshwater swamps over millions of years where burial by more falling leaves produces coal. The alternative suggestion, offered by some scientists, suggests that vegetation was rapidly transported and deposited, under Flood conditions, to form coal.

In brief, the evolutionary method requires huge areas of swamps, over which lush vegetation grew. Falling leaves would enter the freshwater swamps, accumulate and be covered by more rapidly falling leaves. The upper layer of vegetable matter would keep oxygen out and prevent total decay, as well as provide the necessary pressure to convert vegetation to organic muck, peat and eventually coals with higher carbon content.

The above process could not occur in fresh water that contains a lot of oxygen. Swamps, marshes and bogs, where the water is often stagnant and deplete in oxygen, provide an ideal ecological environment for organic muck to form. The low level of oxygen present in such ideal situations, however, does cause some decay of the vegetable matter, but the organic matter accumulates faster than it decomposes. Anaerobic bacteria (which function in the absence of oxygen) can cause decay but their waste must be removed by oxidation (a process requiring oxygen) for them to function. In the absence of oxygen, waste matter accumulates and kills the bacteria, preventing any further decay.

It would take millions of years for enough dead vegetation to accumulate, and for the overlying layers to provide sufficient pressure and temperature to change vegetable matter into peat within the swamps.

Some scientists, who are also creationists, view the formation of coal differently. They say the accumulation of vegetable matter was caused by rapid transportation during the catastrophe of the Genesis Flood. The up-heaval would provide enough sediment to cover the vegetation and provide adequate pressure to expel oxygen and hydrogen from the organic mass, leaving coal behind. This method does not require millions of years nor freshwater swamps to produce coal.

The kinds of conditions that come anywhere near those required by evolutionists to form coal, are found in the rain forests of the tropics where vegetation is lush. However, there are no huge deposits of vegetation happening on the scale required, anywhere in the world that could form even a small seam of coal. Any potential coal-forming swamps are rare.

In Scotland and Ireland there is an abundance of peat which is dug, dried and burned as fuel. There is no evidence, however, of any new coal seams, with 70% or more carbon content being formed in these areas. All known coal-beds (excluding peat) appear to have been formed in the past and are not continuing today. One area that has an appreciable peat deposit is the Dismal Swamp of Virginia in the United States where there is an average of 2m of peat. This, however, is much too little to form even a thin seam of coal, which has been known to vary from a few centimetres to over 12m thick. Calculations show that it would require between 0.6m and 6m of peat to form a 0.3m thickness of coal. That is, it requires about 120m of peat to form a 6m seam. No less than 1463m of plant matter would be needed to accumulate in a swamp to eventually produce such thickness. This seems to be an impossibility, particularly if we base our calculations on uniformitarianism, which states that the rate at which vegetable matter accumulates today is the same as in the past. The average depth of most marshes is 15m,[5] a far cry from the great depths required to accommodate plant matter before it is compacted into peat. Furthermore, coal is found throughout the geological column, worldwide. There is simply not the physical conditions: extensive marshes and enough depth in them, nor enough time to allow plant matter to accumulate, be compacted, pressured and heated to form coal.

On the other hand, water possesses all the requirements to form coal. Given that there was a vast amount of vegetation prior to the Flood (see later) some scientists believe that a catastrophe could have uprooted and transported vegetation in great heaps and buried it at great depths before decay set in. Such a compaction would require only pressure, which the sediment and water would provide, to make coal. No millions of years are necessary for this model to work.

6.6   HOW LONG DID IT TAKE TO FORM A SEAM?

There are no signs in the coal deposits of the world, to indicate that peat has been progressively transformed into coal. In the evolutionary scheme of time, however, peat preceded coal by 50 million years.[6] The earliest coal deposits are found in the upper Devonian rocks in the Arctic region of Canada. If, according to the records, freshwater and land plants evolved 400 million years ago and the earliest coal deposits are dated at 370 million years, then it would seem that coal took about 30 million years to form.

Although coal can be found throughout the geologic column, the Carboniferous and Permian Periods represent the most important interval of coal formation in earth's history. In fact, the Carboniferous Period (see Table 6.1) was given its name in recognition of the abundance of coal deposits formed during that time in Europe.[7] In America, most of the coal deposited is bituminous, laid down during their Pennsylvanous Period (equivalent to the European's Carboniferous Period) from between 286–320 million years[8] (using evolutionary time scale).

We know from the account at the beginning of this chapter that Ms Daisy produced charcoal between 3 and 5 days. Also various laboratory experiments have successfully produced coal materials of various ranks between 2 and 8 months. It is true that both these methods are carefully controlled by humans, but what about nature's activities?

In the well-known Mount St Helen (north-western USA) volcanic eruption

Table 6.1: Periods in the Paleozoic Era of Geologic Time

	Years ago	Duration	Periods
	millions		
PALEOZOIC	280	50	Permian
	310	65	Carboniferous: Pennsylvanian Mississippian
	345	60	Devonian
	425	20	Silurian
	500	75	Ordovician
	600	100	Cambrian

in May 1980, a moderate earthquake triggered the collapse of the north face of this 2948m mountain. Millions of trees over a radius of 24km were flattened, uprooted and transported to Spirit Lake, nestled among forests at the base of the mountain. Some of them were buried; some partially exposed; some with their root intact. Among the matted formation, some remained upright. This catastrophe seems to re-enact the biblical Flood scenes, when vegetation was rapidly transported, covered with sediment and eventually turned into coal.

Today, fossilised tree trunks are found penetrating two or more coal seams, each of which is reported to have taken millions of years to form. No tree could endure exposure to the atmosphere for millions of years while one layer after another of the geologic column was formed. A likely explanation is: as with the upright trunks in Spirit Lake, the Flood of Genesis deposited land vegetation, which was then covered by sediment from the overlying water. Pressure from the sediment caused the organic mass to heat; and within a short period of time (not millions of years) coal formed, trapping some tree trunks transcending more than one seam.

6.7 THE COMPOSITION OF COAL

What do we find in coal? Boulders, trees, leaves, seeds, marine rocks, marine fossils, etc. These are not the actual components of coal, but rather foreign bodies.

Coal itself is a sedimentary rock, composed of compressed, altered remains of living organisms, especially land plants. The change from organic muck to coal, leaves an enriched residue of carbon. No type of coal is all carbon. Anthracite has the highest concentration of carbon (98%) but there are some contaminants such as sulphur.

The evolutionary model for the formation of coal in swamps would produce samples that are rich in swamp-plant fossils. What is actually found is a very great quantity of plant fossils that originated on dry land, plants like chestnut, elder, poplar, magnolia, together with leaves of some palms.[9] Trees and shrubs that now exist in India and Australia (e.g. fig, cinnamon, various palms) are present in the coal of Europe. In addition, most coal-beds reveal a rich variety of marine animal fossils, such as fish remains.

A casual look at the constituent of any coal-bed will clearly state the major contributions to its make up. These are usually components from dry land and seas. There is no clear indication to suggest how coal could be formed in swamps from the type of vegetation that once thrived in that environment. On the other hand, a catastrophe could easily bring both land and marine species together, which, when buried, could produce coal.

6.8 THE WORLD BEFORE THE FLOOD

With the estimated trillions of tons of coal in the earth, we might ask where all the vegetation came from to be compressed into its formation. There is no doubt that the present extremes of temperature we experience did not prevail prior to the Flood. The wide distribution of fossil plants from tropical and temperate zones, even in places such as Antarctica and Alaska, points to a uniform global tropical temperature. For example, the same tropical fossil plants that are found in Greenland are found in Guinea. Fossil plants are also found in the Sahara and Arctic regions.

Any plant species that thrived then, would be found today in the dense growth of the rain forests where warmth and humidity exist. There would be ideal greenhouse conditions to promote the rapid growth of vegetation. The mountains before the Flood would be less peaked and probably covered with vegetation. They certainly would not affect climatic conditions as they do today. There was only one type of climate. Such a climate was conducive to the free roaming of huge cold-blooded animals like dinosaurs. Their size prevented their living in wintry conditions. Yet their fossils are found all over the world, including the polar regions.

Today, just about 25% of the earth's surface is dry land. Only about 50% of this is habitable. The deserts of Africa, the huge inaccessible mountain ranges of North and South America, Northern India, the Alps of Europe, the tundra of Canada and barren plateau of Tibet; the polluted areas of the industrialised nations and the ice caps of the Poles, all contribute to the other 50% of land that humans are unable to use freely.

It has not always been like this. God Himself announced, after He created the earth and its inhabitants that it was very good (Genesis 1:31). After that, sin entered the earth; the Flood was a means of purging the earth of its wickedness. The after effects of the Flood serve as a reminder that before the Flood the environment was less hostile; the climate was even; plants and animals were larger; and there were fewer, if any, concrete structures around. There was very much more land than we have now.

The extremities in climatic conditions that we experience now, are post-Flood phenomena. In Genesis 8:22, we read that after He put the rainbow in the sky and explained its significance, God prepared Noah for the future climatic conditions which would be different from anything he had been used to. God said: "As long as the earth endures, seedtime and harvest, cold and heat, summer and winter, day and night will never cease." The change had taken place. It would remain for as long as this earth lasted.

God created humankind with the inherent ability and intelligence to work things out for themselves; to take decisions and make choices in order to cope with these varied climatic conditions and changing times. This is not an unfair expectation, because we are made in the image of God – with the ability to think, to create, to exercise choice, to love.

6.9 CONCLUSION

In conclusion, here is list of summary points which suggest that coal was not formed in situ in swampy conditions but was the product of rapid transportation and quick burial by a worldwide Flood.

Let the earth speak to us:

◆ Equable climatic conditions before the Flood of warmth, moisture and humidity were identical all over the earth and promoted a profuse growth of vegetation.

◆ More dry land was present and thus more vegetation before the Flood than is the case today.

◆ Coal can be produced only by the accumulation of vegetable matter, for only vegetation can decompose into carbonic acid, leaving carbon as a residue.

◆ Coal is made mainly from trees and plants which do not grow in swamps or peat bogs, and therefore cannot be part of the accumulation of peat-like formations.

◆ Modern peat bogs are not accumulating vegetation on a scale to support a uniformitarian process which is the growth-in-place theory.

◆ Coal deposits of the world are tremendous in magnitude. Alberta alone could supply a million tons each year for 673,000 years.

◆ All the world's minable coal could come from peat covering just 1.27% of the earth's surface (smaller than Australia).

◆ There is no gradation from one rank of coal to another in one place. We find only peat, lignite, bituminous or anthracite in any one area.

◆ Often, fossil tree trunks are found running through two or more seams of coal.

◆ Beds of coal are found associated above and below non-coal material with transported substance. Often, one seam is split into two by such material.

◆ Absence of soil below many coal beds disproves the accumulation-in-place theory.[10]

◆ Foreign boulders in coal seams support the rapid transportation theory

◆ Coal beds are not forming today.

Does the earth speak to us through the above observations?

References

1. Press, Frank; Raymond Siever. *Earth* (Freeman, San Francisco, 1978).

2. Rehwinkel, Alfred M. *The Flood* (Concordia Publishing House, Missouri, 1951).

3. Senkins, Frederick J; Clement G Chase; David G Darby and George Tapp Jr. *The Evolving Earth* (Macmillan, New York, 1978).

4. Major, Trevor J. Genesis and the *Origin of Coal and Oil* (Apologetics Press, Alabama, 1990).

5. *Ibid*.

6. *Ibid*.

7. Senkins, *op cit*.

8. Monroe, James S; Reed Wincander. *Physical Geology: Exploring the Earth* (West Pub. Co., St Paul, 1992).

9. Rehwinkel, *op. cit.*

10. Patten, Donald W. (ed.). *Symposium on Creation III* (Baker Books, Michigan, 1971)

7

EXTRATERRESTRIAL IMPACTS AND THE FLOOD

7.1   METEOR SHOWERS

On the night of 13 November, 1833, a spectacular shower of light flashes was seen in the skies over North America.[1] Observers reported seeing many brilliant fireballs, some of which exploded with a bang. Unusual odours were also detected in the atmosphere. This event happened when a storm of space dust struck Earth's atmosphere.

When objects from space strike Earth's atmosphere, they are heated until they glow. As they move through the atmosphere, they produce a streak of light. The object with its light is known as a meteor, or a "falling star". The object which strikes Earth's atmosphere is known as a meteoroid. Meteoroids may come from fragments of comets that have disintegrated. Most meteoroids become so hot that they burn up before they reach the surface of the earth.

The 1833 dust storm was a Leonid meteor storm. Leonid meteor storms occur annually, although usually with much lower intensity than what happened in 1833. High-intensity Leonid meteor storms occur about every 33 years. On the night of 16 November, 1966, an even greater meteor display occurred over western North America. Unfortunately, clouds obscured the view over most of the area, but a few scientists on Kitt Peak in Arizona were able to observe the brightness of the storm. For about an hour, 500 meteors per minute were seen. This peaked at 2,500 per minute. This is believed to be the most spectacular meteor shower in recorded history. The most recent spectacular show of the Leonid meteor storm was in November, 1999.

The individual particles that produced the meteor showers of 1833 and 1966 were probably very small, perhaps the size of a grain of sand. Such small objects cannot harm living matter or humans on the surface of Earth, because they are destroyed by frictional heat on contact with the atmosphere. What about larger objects? Can they penetrate the atmosphere and strike the surface of Earth? They certainly can.

7.2 METEORITE IMPACTS

Stony or metallic objects that strike Earth are called meteorites. Meteorites strike Earth more frequently than most people realise. For example, a small meteorite struck a parked car in Peekskill, New York, on 9 October, 1992. Fortunately, no-one was hurt, although the car received some damage. Others have not been so fortunate.[2] A member of a bridal party was killed in Zvezvan, Yugoslavia, on 8 December, 1929. Two people were reportedly killed by the famous 30 June, 1908, blast in Tunguska, Siberia. There is even a report that a shower of stony meteorites killed over 10,000 people in China in the year 1409. There seem to be no reports of casualties from meteorites in Britain, but a boy was knocked off his bicycle by a meteorite explosion on 30 November, 1946. Some people think a meteorite was involved in the destruction of the Amorites, as described in Joshua 10:11.

A faint idea of the power of meteorite impact can be obtained from the 1908 Tunguska explosion in Russia. This explosion occurred some 5–10km above the surface of the earth, and flattened the trees over an area of at least 2,000 square kilometres. The explosion is believed to have been caused by a single stony meteoroid, about 30m in diameter.[3] The meteoroid presumably fragmented in the atmosphere, exploded and vaporised, leaving no crater on the earth and very little in the way of identifiable fragments (meteorites).

What eventually happens to the material of a meteoroid depends in part on its mass. Small objects, such as dust particles, burn up before striking the ground. Larger, ten metre-sized objects may lose part of their mass as they pass through the atmosphere, but part of the material may survive and impact the earth and thus be recovered. The largest known single meteorite mass, the Hoba meteorite of South Africa, is less than 3m in length. Kilometre-sized objects do not survive impact with Earth. Very large objects strike Earth with such force that they are vaporised on impact. Huge amounts of energy are released, forming craters and blowing rocks and dust into the atmosphere. Such events may also cause enormous ecological damage.

Impact craters have been reported from several places in Europe, including Sweden, Poland, Germany and France. At the time of writing this chapter no impact craters have been reported from Britain. The first impact crater to be identified was a meteorite crater, near Winslow, Arizona, in the United States. The Winslow crater is about 1.25km in diameter and 175m deep. It is believed to be the result of the impact of a metallic meteorite about 30m in diameter. The crater and its rim are well preserved, suggesting that it was formed relatively recently, although certainly before the arrival of Europeans. When meteorite fragments of iron and nickel were discovered near the crater, an enterprising miner attempted to locate the main mass of the meteorite he thought was buried under the crater. He was disappointed to discover that most of the metal was not there. His experience illustrates a paradox of extraterrestrial impacts: only the relatively small meteorites survive an impact.

Most of the meteorites that have struck Earth, in recorded history, have been relatively small in size. However, some very large objects, such as comets and asteroids, are also present in space. Typical asteroids are large pieces of stone or metal, between 1km and 100km in diameter. Many such objects are found in the "asteroid belt", a region of space between the orbital paths of Mars and Jupiter. Comets, sometimes called "dirty snow balls", are thought to be aggregations of space material, with large amounts of water. The main body of a comet, the head, may be as large as 10km in diameter. It is the comet's long tail of gases, debris and water that makes it so visible to the naked eye. Comets travel in paths that take them outside our solar system, crossing the orbits of the planets. Both comets and asteroids travel at very high speeds, typically from 50,000 to 180,000 km per hour. This means they possess enormous amounts of energy. A 250m comet or asteroid has typically more kinetic energy than would be released from the explosion of all the world's nuclear weapons. If such an object were to strike Earth, it could be expected to leave a crater perhaps 5 or 10km in diameter. There is evidence that such impacts, and even larger ones, have occurred.

7.3 EVIDENCE OF NUMEROUS IMPACTS IN THE GEOLOGIC RECORD

Identification of craters caused by extraterrestrial impacts, must have complementary evidence. The most obvious identifying mark is the crater itself. However, craters can also be formed by volcanic activity, so mere discovery of a crater is not enough to identify an extraterrestrial impact.[5] Volcanic craters, however, would be located in volcanic rock. If no volcanic rocks are present at a crater, one would suspect it was formed by an impact. Iridium is an element that is rare in Earth's crust, but is more abundant in space materials. The presence of high concentrations of iridium in clay has been used to identify extraterrestrial impacts. Volcanoes may also release some iridium.[6] Extraterrestrial impacts also produce certain substances that require very high energies to form them. These include the mineral coesite shock fracturing of quartz grains, and pieces of molten rock, called tektites. Of course, discovery of a meteorite fragment at a crater site would confirm that an impact had occurred there.

Based on the presence of shocked quartz grains, tektites, etc., scientists have identified more than 100 impact craters on Earth's surface.[7] These range in size from a few metres to more than 100km in diameter. Some of them, such as the 1.25km Meteor Crater in Arizona, are well preserved. Others, such as the 100km Manicouagan Crater in Quebec or the 2 km Lonar Crater in India, are noticeably eroded. A few buried craters have been reported, including the famous 180km Chicxulub Crater of Yucatan, Mexico.[8] Scientists have also identified a few craters buried under the floor of the sea, such as the 45km Montagnais crater near Nova Scotia[9] or the 85km Chesapeake Bay crater.[10] These craters are clear evidence that numerous extraterrestrial objects have struck Earth.

Extraterrestrial impact craters are found throughout the geologic column and are distributed widely across the surface of Earth. A few craters are found in Precambrian (lowest layer) rocks, and at least 30 are found in each of the major systems – the Paleozoic, Mesozoic and Cenozoic. Several are found in Quaternary sediments, at the very top of the geologic column. Impact craters have been discovered on every inhabited continent, with the largest numbers in Europe and North America. The most famous impact structures in Western Europe are probably the Ries Crater of Germany and the Siljan structure in Sweden. There are undoubtedly many more craters to be discovered, and many buried ones that may never be found. Since these structures are found throughout the geologic column, extraterrestrial impacts must have occurred throughout the time during which fossils were being buried by sediment.

7.4   CATASTROPHIC EFFECTS OF LARGE IMPACTS

Meteorite impacts can have catastrophic effects. Just imagine the destruction caused by the Tunguska explosion, with trees flattened over an area of 2000 square km. The energy of this explosion has been estimated as equivalent to a 10–15 megaton nuclear bomb. Such destruction pales into insignificance when compared with the impact of a large asteroid. It is estimated that objects as large as 10km in diameter have struck Earth in the past. The amount of damage from such an impact is outside human experience.

although scientists have made calculations of some of the expected effects. An analysis of the effects of extraterrestrial impacts could help us to understand how the geologic column was formed.

The largest impact crater yet identified is the Chicxulub Crater in Mexico, with a diameter of about 180km. The size of the object has been estimated, based on the amount of iridium found in the clay associated with the impact, to be 10km in diameter. Such an impact might release an amount of energy approximately equivalent to ten million Tunguska exploding at once. This might create a blast of wind, hot enough to scorch Earth for thousands of kilometres around. According to some estimates, most surface life over half of Earth would be destroyed. A cloud of dust would be thrown up into the atmosphere, where it would remain for months, obscuring the light of the sun and producing winter-like weather conditions. This would probably result in mass deaths by starvation or freezing temperatures. Large numbers of species would probably become extinct, an event known as a mass extinction. It has been argued that the extinction of the dinosaurs might be linked to such an impact. The impact of a 10km object might also generate earthquakes that might extend worldwide.[12] These would be accompanied by giant tidal surges, known as tsunamis, that would strip the surface sediment from coastal areas and deposit large quantities of sediment rapidly. Sediment closer to the impact site might resemble certain glacial deposits known as tillites. Tillites are piles of unsorted rubble, produced when glaciers push rocks of various sizes into piles. It has recently been proposed that similar piles of rubble can be produced by extraterrestrial impacts, so that tillites do not necessarily indicate the presence of glaciers.[13] This might explain the unexpected presence of tillites in several places of the geologic column. These tillites have been somewhat problematic. Creationists would not expect glaciers to have enough time to form during the Flood, and evolutionists have been puzzled by the apparent association of ice ages with fossils that are more typical of moderate climates, not cold climates.

Some scientists have speculated further about the possible effects of very large extraterrestrial impacts.[14] Certain very large volcanic flows, known as flood basalts, may be associated with extraterrestrial impacts. Impacts may also have contributed to the movement of Earth's geologic plates. Other scientists have proposed that impacts may have caused geomagnetic reversals.[15] No better explanation seems available for these phenomena. Extraterrestrial impacts provide the best answers known at present. However, these conjectures have not been confirmed scientifically.

7.5   EXTRATERRESTRIAL IMPACTS AND MASS EXTINCTIONS

Different types of fossils are located at different positions in the geologic column. Often, the types of fossils change rather abruptly from one layer to another. The change may involve the abrupt appearance of additional types of fossils, or the abrupt disappearance of fossil groups. When a species disappears from the fossil record, it is generally presumed to have become extinct. In some cases, many kinds of organisms disappear at the same point in the geologic column. This pattern is known as a mass extinction. Numerous examples of mass extinction patterns are seen in the fossil record, and scientists have wondered what could cause them. An extraterrestrial impact has been proposed as a likely cause.

The main fossil-bearing portion of the geologic column is divided into three segments, or rock systems – the Paleozoic, Mesozoic and Cenozoic systems. Each of these three geologic systems is separated from the others by a major change in the types of fossils found in it, identified as a mass extinction.

The most famous mass extinction pattern is at the top of the Mesozoic rock system. The upper rocks of the Mesozoic rock system are called Cretaceous rocks. The Cenozoic rocks immediately above the Cretaceous are known as Tertiary rocks. Dinosaur fossils are commonly found in Cretaceous rocks, but not in rocks of the Tertiary system. Dinosaurs disappear completely from the fossil record at the top of the Mesozoic. Several other groups also disappear from the fossil record, along with the dinosaurs. These include extinct groups of reptiles such as the pterosaurs, plesiosaurs and ichthyosaurs, as well as certain groups of molluscs called ammonites. The simultaneous disappearances of these groups are a classic example of an extinction pattern, and have been linked with an extraterrestrial impact.

The top of the Cretaceous rock system in several locations is marked by indications of a large extraterrestrial impact. Unusually high concentrations of iridium are found. The Chicxulub crater is also found approximately at the top of the Cretaceous rocks. Thus, many scientists link the extinction of the dinosaurs to the formation of the Chicxulub crater by an extraterrestrial impact. A large flood basalt, the Deccan traps of India, is also found at the top of the Cretaceous, and some scientists have proposed that it may be linked to the mass extinction. The coincidence of the impact and the flood basalt has led other scientists to suggest that the impact might have caused the flood basalt, and the combination of the two phenomena caused the end-Cretaceous mass extinction.

The most dramatic extinction pattern is found at the top of the Permian rocks, which form the top of the Paleozoic. This extinction pattern is called the end-Permian extinction.[16] Many kinds of animals disappear from the fossil record at the top of the Paleozoic, but they are not so familiar or spectacular as the dinosaurs; so most people have not given them very much attention. It has been estimated that perhaps 95% of all the species found in uppermost Paleozoic rocks are not found in rocks above that point in the geologic column. This represents a major change in the kinds of organisms being fossilised. No impact crater has been identified at the top of the Paleozoic layers.[17] However, the largest flood basalt on the continents, the Siberian traps, is associated with the top of the Paleozoic. There are some indications that may link other mass extinctions to flood basalts, and possibly to extraterrestrial impacts as well.[18]

7.6   EXTRATERRESTRIAL IMPACTS AND THE FLOOD

We have noted that extraterrestrial impacts seem to have occurred throughout the deposition of the geologic column, and throughout the world. In addition, there appears to be a relationship between certain geologic events, such as flood basalts and extraterrestrial impacts, and abrupt changes in the kinds of fossils being deposited. These deductions suggest that the Genesis Flood was accompanied by a "shower" of extraterrestrial objects. This concept may contribute to our understanding, as we attempt to develop a picture of what the worldwide Flood of Genesis must have been like. We should keep in mind that most of the impacts were much smaller and had more localised effects than those hypothesised for the end-Cretaceous impact. Indeed, it is conceivable that calculations of the end-Cretaceous impact have over-estimated its effects. The following description is offered as an example of how extraterrestrial impacts might have contributed to the catastrophe of Genesis.

The major features of the fossil record should provide important clues about the nature of the Flood. One of the more important difficulties in understanding the Flood is that there appear to be many places in the geologic column where living organisms were active. Many footprints have been left by marine creatures, along with burrows and pellets. Footprints of terrestrial animals are also quite common. Many dinosaur footprints are known, and even what appear to be dinosaur nests. These and other examples indicate that the Flood did not destroy all living organisms at the same time.

Different kinds of organisms died and were buried at different times during the Flood. Before they died, they might have moved about, looking for food or refuge from the storms of the Flood. It has been difficult for some creationists to imagine how so many animals could survive through so much of the Flood, only to die later. Extraterrestrial impacts may help them to understand this problem.

A series of impacts provides a mechanism for destroying the world in stages. The results would depend on the geographical location and environmental effects of the impacts. Each impact would cause a sequence of extremely large-scale geological effects, perhaps followed by a period of less intense geologic activity. Thus, the Flood might have involved a series of geological catastrophes, separated by short periods in which the survivors would wander about, looking for food, attempting to build nests, or searching for a better environment. This effect could be called the "stepwise Flood".

Another possible effect of extraterrestrial impacts is destruction of some kinds of animals while others might survive. For example, an impact on land might be more effective in destroying groups from certain habitats. Earthquakes caused by the impact, might produce landslides that would bury large numbers of creatures living on the bottom of the ocean or lakes. Of course, many of these creatures might simply burrow through the overlying mud, leaving behind those species that did not survive, as well as forming burrows to be fossilised. Those species able to swim might survive such an event. This might provide a means of separating different types of marine creatures. Many terrestrial creatures might be killed by the blast, while those that burrow under the surface might survive longer. Bodies of the terrestrial species might be buried later, when the rising Flood waters reached them.

An impact into the ocean might kill many of the marine creatures that could survive an impact on land. Shock waves would pass through the water and kill many fish and other good swimmers. Water temperature could even be raised by the heat of the impact. Giant waves would be formed, which would wash over coastal areas, pulling the plants and animals into the ocean, where many would be buried quickly. The nature of the sequence of impacts might play a decisive role in determining the sequence of fossils that would be produced. This effect could be called the "sequential extinction" effect.

A third possible effect of extraterrestrial impacts in the Flood would be large-scale geologic effects. The great amounts of energy released by impacts could produce large volumes of sediment and rapidly transport them over considerable distances. Vast quantities of sediment could be deposited in short periods of time. Recurring cycles of sediment could be produced by a series of tsunamis. Ocean currents could transport carcasses over long distances. This effect could be called the "large-scale geology" effect. A series of extraterrestrial impacts, accompanied by hurricanes and other phenomena, would undoubtedly have additional effects beyond those we have proposed. Perhaps our suggestions on how they might have related to the Flood, are entirely wrong. Nevertheless, the point has been made that large-scale, high-energy events seem intimately associated with the deposition of the geologic column. Future discoveries may present us with new ideas. As our understanding of the geologic column grows, we can expect that our understanding of the Flood will also grow. However, it is likely that we shall never have a complete understanding of an event that has happened only once.

7.7 CONCLUSION

Annual meteor showers remind us that Earth has been struck many times by objects from space. More than 100 impact craters have been identified in the fossil layers. This indicates that the Genesis Flood was accompanied by a shower of extraterrestrial objects that had great destructive powers. Such a meteorite shower might explain how the Flood could have produced certain features of the geologic record.

Extraterrestrial impacts could also be expected to have certain effects that might be important in understanding the nature of the fossil record. Impacts would provide a source of huge amounts of energy, delivered in blasts that were separated by short periods of time. Thus, they might produce pulses of tremendous geologic activity, separated by periods of lesser activity. Such pulses of activity might produce abrupt changes in the kinds of rocks or fossils being deposited. The large amounts of energy released by an extraterrestrial impact would cause geologic activity on a more extensive scale than has occurred within recorded history. Large amounts of sediment might be moved around in a short time. A series of tidal waves might occur, rapidly depositing several layers of sediment. Some materials might be transported over vast areas.

It seems likely that extraterrestrial impacts played an important role in the Flood, but the nature of this role is still largely unknown. No-one has actually observed the impact of a large extraterrestrial object on Earth, so one cannot be confident about the nature of the effects. Certainly, there are many features of the geologic record that we do not understand. These features include what seems to be a pattern of pulses of intense large-scale geologic activity and deposition. Such suggestions are unproven at this time, but provide ideas for further exploration regarding the nature of the catastrophe of Genesis.

Extraterrestrial impacts serve to remind us that God surely has many ways of accomplishing His will that are beyond our experience or understanding.

References
1. Lewis, J. S. *Rain of iron and ice*. (Helix Books. Addison-Wesley Publ Co. Reading, Mass. 1996).
2. *Ibid*.
3. Chyba, C. F., P. J. Thomas and K. J. Zahnle. "The 1908 Tunguska explosion: atmospheric disruption of a stony asteroid", Nature 361:40–44. (1993).
4. McCall, G. J. H. *Meteorites and their origins*. (David and Charles: Newton Abbot, Devon., UK, 1973.)
5. . Alvarez, L. W., W. Alvarez, F. Asaro, and H. V. Michel. "Extraterrestrial cause for the Cretaceous-Tertiary extinction". Science 208:1095–1108. (1980).
6. Zoller, W. H., J. R. Parrington, and J. M. Phelan Kotra. "Iridium enrichment in airborne particles from Kilauea volcano: January 1983." Science 222:1181–1121 (1983).
7. Grieve, R. A. F. "Terrestrial impact structures." Annual Review of Earth and Planetary Science 15:245–270 (1987).
8. Hildebrand, A. R., G. T. Penfield, D. A. Kring, M. Pilkington, A. Camargo Z., S. B. Jacobsen, and W. V. Boynton. Chicxulub Crater: A possible Cretaceous/Tertiary boundary impact crater on the Yucatan Peninsula, Mexico. *Geology* 19:867–871 (1991).
9. Jansa, L. F. and G. Pe-Piper. "Identification of an underwater extraterrestrial impact crater." *Nature* 327:612–614 (1987).
10. Poag, C. W., D. S. Powars, L. J. Poppe, and R. B. Mixon. "Meteoroid mayhem in Ole Virginny: Source of the North American tektite strewn field." Geology 22:691–694 (1994).
11. Clube, V. and B. Napier. "Close encounters with a million comets." *New Scientist* 95:148–151 (1982).
12. *Ibid*.
13. Rampino, M. R. "Tillites, diamictites, and ballistic ejecta of large impacts." Journal of Geology 102:439–456 (1994).

14. Oberbeck, V. R., J. R. Marshall and H. Aggarwal. "Impacts, tillites, and the breakup of Gondwanaland." Journal of Geology 101:1–19 (1993).
15. Loper, D. E., K. McCartney and G. Buzyna. "A model of correlated episoduscity in magnetic-field reversals, climate, and mass extinctions." Journal of Geology 96:1–15 (1988).
16. Erwin, D. H. "The great Paleozoic crisis. Columbia University Press (1993).
17. Rampino, M. R. "A major Late Permian impact event on the Falkland Plateau." Eos 74(43, suppl.):336 (1993).
18. Rampino, M. R. and R. B. Stothers. "Flood basalt volcanism during the past 250 million years." Science 241:663–668 (1988).

8

TAMING THE T-REX

What do we really know about Tyrannosaurus rex (Figure 8.1)? Was it the biggest, meanest, meat-eating dinosaur on earth? Apparently not. Some recently discovered dinosaur bones were named Giganotosaurus: now considered the largest carnivorous (meat-eating) dinosaur ever found. Whether this is so or not, many people want to know, "Where did these giant carnivores come from?" Even people who believe our world was created by an Intelligent Designer often ask, "Did God create T-rex?" As more and more bones are discovered, the role that T-rex and other dinosaurs played in earth's history has aroused the curiosity of many people to find out more.

8.1   EXPLORING THE DINOSAUR DATABASE

Dinosaurs are identified by their bones. By 1988, about 2,100 genuine dinosaur bones had been identified. In 1994, Dodson counted 315 different kinds (genera) of dinosaurs worldwide. (Classification of dinosaurs includes the major divisions of : classes ☞ orders ☞ families ☞ genera ☞ species) More than half of these identifications are based on no more than just one or two bones. Although there are thousands of bones, only 63 essentially complete dinosaur skeletons have been found.[1] The data suggest that there was a wide variety of dinosaurs before they became extinct. The existence of so many different groups of dinosaurs before the Genesis Flood, suggests that there might have been some "kinds" of dinosaurs that formed a part of God's original Creation.

The first appearance in the rock record of at least 20 genera of dinosaurs, occurs in the same unit of rock layers on four continents.[2] Evolutionary theory would not predict the appearance of a variety of the same organism, at the same time, in diverse geographic localities. Discovery of this type is difficult to explain from an evolutionary perspective.

Christians, however, interpret these fossil remains as the bodies of the first dinosaurs to be buried during the Flood; the regional distribution of fossils, conforms to this interpretation.

Figure 8.1: TYRANNOSAURUS REX, a bipedal carnivore, had teeth 7 inches long.

Figure 8.2: VELOCIRAPTOR might have joined other raptors and attacked large herbivores.

(Five man height)

Figure 8.3: DIPLODOCUS, a quadrupedal herivore, had pegshaped teeth and nostrils positioned above its eyes.

Figure 8.4: Tracks of a carnivore near Glen Rose, Texas, USA

Figure 8.5: Sauuropod egg found in Argentina. The egg is on display at the Regional Museumin Valcheta, Rio Negro Province, Argentina.

(Half a man's height)

Figure 8.6: ORODROMEUS might have laid eggs in a spiral pattern

Figure 8.7: MAISASAURA, "good mother lizard", may have cared for babies at the nest site.

Some people are troubled by the extra-large sized dinosaurs. They are uncomfortable with the idea that God might have created huge carnivores such as T-rex, Giganotosaurus and Allosaurus, or even some of the "smaller" meat-eaters like Velociraptor (Figure 8.2). If they accept that God created dinosaurs during Creation week and that all animals were herbivores (Genesis 1:30), then when did dinosaurs become carnivores? One possible explanation for the carnivorous diet is that during the time between Creation week and the Flood, the effects of sin altered the appearance and habits of many organisms, including the dinosaurs. What about the issue of giant dinosaurs? Some 31 of the 58 known dinosaur families have no members exceeding 6 metres in length, which is the size of a contemporary African elephant.[3] With this in mind, perhaps it is not so difficult to picture a pre- or post-Flood world that included these smaller carnivorous and herbivorous (plant-eating) dinosaurs, even if it is difficult to see the larger ones in those environments.

The bones of dinosaurs can tell us a lot about how they lived. In order to understand dinosaurs better, scientists reconstruct the skeletons from the available bones. The task of identifying and reassembling the dinosaur bones is a challenging one. The resulting reconstructions are not just a poorly constructed hodge-podge of bones, as some have suggested. Portions of skulls, hips, thighs, legs and feet are used to identify and classify dinosaurs. The differences in the hip structure of dinosaurs have been used to organise them into two major groups: Saurischia (lizard hip) and Ornithischia (bird hip).

All the carnivorous dinosaurs, including Tyrannosaurus rex, have the lizard-like hip structure and are assigned to the order Saurischia. Another group of well-known dinosaurs assigned to the saurischians were the enormous sauropods (large, long-necked, plant-eating dinosaurs), like Diplodocus (Figure 8.3). According to some scientists,[4] Supersaurus, a sauropod with a length of up to 42 metres, weighed almost 50 metric tons (about the weight of 7 African elephants).[5] It must have taken a lot of food to keep these animals alive and moving. Even the smallest auropods, approximately 9 metres in length, must have eaten an enormous amount of vegetation to survive.

However, the plant material found in the rocks, together with the dinosaurs' bones, is not representative of the volume and variety of plant life that must have been needed for these animals.[6] For those who believe that millions of years separated the burial of much of the plant material and the dinosaurs, this lack of plants poses a big problem. Those who accept biblical history believe the plant and animal remains found in the rock layers all co-existed in the pre-Flood world. So the sparse occurrence of plant fossils with dinosaur bones might indicate some sorting of the materials during the Flood.

There is more to the dinosaur database than just bones. In addition to the bone fragments, isolated bones, bone-beds and complete skeletons that have been recovered, scientists have discovered trackways, skin impressions, gastroliths (gizzard stones in excreta), juvenile dinosaurs, hatchlings, embryos, eggs and nests.

Bone graveyards that have been discovered have yielded dinosaur bones for museum collections around the world. An example of one of these beds is found in the badlands of Alberta, Canada. Approximately 80 Centrosaurs (sometimes called Encentrosaurus) were found with Tyrannosaurus rex bite marks on their bones. T-rex normally lost its teeth during feeding. Some of these shed teeth were found in association with the bones of Centrosaurus. Scientists think that the Centrosaurs died while trying to cross a flooded river and their dead bodies would naturally attract a carnivore like T-rex.[7]

Another bone bed was uncovered in 1984. It contained partial remains, estimated to represent at least 10,000 Maiasaurs. The "herd" of Maiasaurs found in the bone bed, were entombed in volcanic ash/mud flow and apparently died during a volcanic eruption.[8] The formation of bone beds (sometimes referred to as fossil graveyards or mass mortalities) is often associated with catastrophes. Deposits that have been interpreted by some scientists as localised catastrophes, might have been laid down during a worldwide flood.

In the past, there was much scepticism with respect to the existence of dinosaurs. This is understandable when one takes into consideration the size of these animals and their diet. Today, it is difficult to deny that they existed. There is insurmountable evidence to support the fact that dinosaurs were living, breathing animals in the pre-Flood world.

8.2 DID DINOSAURS REALLY LIVE?

Dinosaur tracks are found in about 1,000 locations worldwide.[9] Tracks indicate that dinosaurs were alive and moving through these areas when the sediment was still soft enough to take an imprint (Figure 8.4). Unfortunately, no dinosaur has been found "stopped dead in its tracks"; so making a positive identification of the animal responsible for the track is difficult. Researchers, however, are able to make a wide variety of interpretations from these trackways. Scientists measure the size, spacing and arrangement of the tracks to determine the unique gait of the animal. The shape, the depth and the gait of the prints are used to determine whether the animal was walking or running. Most tracks seem to have been made by dinosaurs moving briskly.[10] Variations in the sizes of the prints may suggest the herding of adult and juvenile dinosaurs in a single trackway. However, it might not be possible to determine whether small, isolated tracks belonged to a small adult or a juvenile.[11]

The most unexpected information to come from the tracksites, is a pattern of limping behaviour. Both four-footed (quadrupedal) and two-footed (bipedal) dinosaurs exhibit an alternating pattern of long and short steps. Such limping patterns raise many questions.[12]

Researchers assume that the locale where they find these trackways is the ancient environment and natural habitat of that particular dinosaur. Trackways have been found in muds and sands that researchers have claimed to be ancient river flood plains, lake shores, and coastal plains.[13] But suppose there had been a catastrophe such as a great Flood, and the dinosaurs were acting under great stress, milling around or moving to higher ground, then their tracks would not reveal natural, normal behaviour, and when they died in rising waters they might have been far from their natural habitat. This view is supported by Lambert,[14] who notes that several dinosaur deposits have been interpreted as Flood deposits.

"Did dinosaurs live?" is a question that should be regarded as obsolete. Whether or not they survived the Flood is one that is better pursued.

8.3 DID DINOSAURS SURVIVE THE FLOOD?

Some Christian scientists have used the Bible texts referring to animals called "behemoth" and "leviathan" (Job 40 and 41) as biblical support for the existence of dinosaurs, both before and after the Flood. Others have suggested that dragon legends are historical evidence for the coexistence of dinosaurs and people. It would not be difficult to find evidence for the existence of dinosaurs after the Genesis Flood, if we could find the articulated skeleton of a Velociraptor impaled on the tusk of a fully articulated woolly mammoth, an animal commonly associated with human history. In reality, dinosaur remains have not been found in rocks with human remains. This fact does not necessarily rule out the possibility that some dinosaurs may have survived in the ark. It has been said, however, that God would not have accommodated dinosaurs on the ark when He knew the climate after the Flood would not be conducive to the survival of large cold-blooded animals.

It seems reasonable to assume that not all of the earth's surface was exposed simultaneously as the Flood waters receded. In other words, rocks that are visible today may represent material deposited, 1) during the Flood, 2) as flood waters subsided, or 3) sometime after the close of the Flood year. If some dinosaurs survived the Flood (in the ark), preservation of their bones and eggs should occur at or near the top of the rock record in the area where they died (Figure 8.5). There is the possibility that such a scenario does exist. A study of dinosaur nests may produce some evidence in support of the idea that they survived the Genesis Flood together with other land animals in Noah's ark, even though this is not conclusive. For example, the Willow Creek Anticline in Montana might have served as a nesting area for Maiasaura and Troodon.[15]

Troodon (Figure 8.6) was a bipedal flesh-eater about 2m in length with large eyes and a retractable second toe,[16] which built nests with a maximum of 24 eggs laid in a spiral pattern, pointing down.[17] Some of the unhatched eggs contained identifiable embryos. Since researchers have found some eggshell material that is broken but not crushed, they have suggested that the young might have left the nest soon after hatching.

The second nest-building dinosaur at the Montana site was Maiasaura, a 9m long herbivore.[18] Several Maiasaurs might have constructed as many as 11 nests on a single level (Figure 8.7). Four of the bowl-shaped nests were found with eggshells, but four others contained hatchlings. One of the nests had 11 hatchlings inside with 4 more babies nearby. Three partially occupied nests were found. In one nest, 10 eggs were found arranged in a paired, linear pattern with an 11th egg nearby. Unlike the Troodon young, baby Maiasaura might have remained at the nest site to be cared for by adults. This idea was originally suggested for two reasons: eggshells associated with the Maiasaur hatchlings are crushed more than the Troodon shells and, in at least one nest, the teeth of the babies were worn, indicating that they were being fed at the nest site for some time after hatching.[19] This latter point turned out not to be as important as first thought, as researchers subsequently found worn teeth in unhatched young, indicating gnawing by the baby dinosaur prior to hatching.[20]

The fact that these are eggs of dinosaurs seems to be well established. In addition, the patterns in which these Troodon eggs were found suggest that these are indeed nests, and not just eggs randomly transported by water. Egg Mountain, one of the nest sites of the Willow Creek Anticline, is characterised by more than one layer of nests.[21] It is possible that the nests represent successive nesting activities of various groups of dinosaurs that entered the area at the height of the Flood. Preservation of the nests required rapid burial of the eggs and young in place. The Genesis Flood could have provided the conditions necessary for this type of preservation. This scenario implies that dinosaurs did not survive the Flood. An alternative model suggests that the nests may represent successive nesting seasons after the Flood, but the question of their preservation would be a problem.

A post-Flood interpretation for the nesting sites, provides limited support for any post-Flood dinosaur survival. The absence of more recent evidence of post-Flood burial, may imply their survival was short-lived, if at all. Extinctions are to be expected in the dramatically altered and unstable post-Flood world of any surviving dinosaurs.

8.4 WHAT HAPPENED TO THE DINOSAURS?

Numerous ideas have been suggested to explain the extinction of the dinosaurs:[22] environmental processes such as changes in sea level, climatic fluctuations, variation in ocean chemistry (pH, salinity, temperature), effects of plate tectonics and volcanism. Extraterrestrial explanations have included supernovas, solar flares, movement of the solar system through the arms of a spiral galaxy and meteorite or asteroid impacts. The two dominant theories today are volcanism and impacts. Both theories involve a change in climate that produces a greenhouse effect, resulting in catastrophic, worldwide loss of life.[23] Some scientists argue that neither theory can explain the extinction of the dinosaurs, because most of them were extinct before these events took place.

From a Christian perspective, there is another explanation for the extinction of dinosaurs that is found in Genesis 7 and 8. The destruction and preservation of the dinosaurs that is recorded in the rocks of the earth could have occurred during this worldwide Flood. As various groups of dinosaurs died worldwide, multiple physical forces could have contributed to their demise. Much evidence of environmental processes and multiple impacts is found in the geologic record. Such evidence, placed in the context of a worldwide Flood, would have devastating results for all life, including dinosaurs, and is perhaps a better answer than any single postulated event.

8.5 CONCLUSION

The history of dinosaurs is fascinating and many people have some strong opinions about these "terrible lizards". As Christians, we need to be cautious because dinosaurs are not addressed by name in the Scriptures. Those descriptions usually attributed to the dinosaurs, may also be applied to other organisms that are preserved in the fossil record. Even though we may not fully understand the role of dinosaurs in earth's history, it is clear that they lived.

The Genesis Flood is presented in Scripture as a judgement against humanity's sin, a judgement that largely destroyed the pre-Flood plant and animal kingdoms. The devastation of animals, that are now extinct, was only a small part of the destruction that took place. It is equally clear in the Flood account that God directly intervened to save a remnant of His Creation. Just as dinosaurs suffered in the destruction, some may have been included in God's effort to save a part of His Creation. Further research is needed to determine whether or not some of the smaller dinosaurs survived.

References

1. Dodson, Peter. "What the Fossil Record of Dinosaurs Tells Us:" in DinoFest, Gary Rosenberg and Donald Wolberg (eds.) *The Paleontological Society* Special Publication 7:21–37 (1994).

2. Hunt, Adrian and Lucas, Spencer. "Synchronous First Appearance of Dinosaurs Worldwide During the Late Triassic" (Late Carnian: Tuvalian): Geological Society of America, Abstracts with Program, A 457 (1991).

3. Nowak, Ronald and Paradiso, John. Walker's Mammals of the World. (Johns Hopkins University Press, Baltimore, 4th edition, 1983), II:1139.

4. Lambert, David and the Diagram Group. Dinosaur Data Book. (Avon Books, New York, 1990), 320.

5. Nowak, et al, *op. cit.*

6. Dodson, Peter, Behrensmeyer, A.K., Bakker, Robert, and McIntosh, John. "Taphonomy and paleoecology of the dinosaur beds of the Jurassic Morrison Formation". Paleobiology 6:208–232 (1980). 7. Gore, Rick. Dinosaurs. National Geographic (January): 42–46 (1993).

8. *Ibid.*
9. Lockley, Martin. Tracking Dinosaurs (Cambridge University Press, New York, 1991), 238.
10. Time (April 26):48 (1993).
11. Irby, Grace. "Tracks and trackmakers at a mass dinosaur tracksite, lower Jurassic Dinosaur Canyon Member Moenave Formation, Northeast Arizona". *Journal of Vertebrate Paleontology*, Abstracts 13(3):43A (1993).
12. Lockley, Martin and Hunt, Adrian. *Dinosaur Tracks.* (Columbia University Press, New York, 1995), 288.
13. Gillette, David and Lockley, Martin (eds.). *Dinosaur Tracks and Traces* (Cambridge University Press, New York, 1989) 454.
14. Lambert et al, *op. cit.*
15. Hirsch, Karl and Quinn, Betty. "Eggs and eggshell fragments from the upper Cretaceous Two Medicine Formation of Montana." *Journal of Vertebrate Paleontology* 10: 491–511 (1990).
16. Lambert et al, *op. cit.*
17. Personal communication from personnel at the Museum of the Rockies, Bozeman, Montana. There has apparently been some confusion with regard to the classification of some of the dinosaur material at this locality.
18. Lambert et al, *op. cit.*
19. Gore, *op. cit.*
20. Horner, John, and Currie, Phillip. *Embryonic and Neonatal Morphology and Ontogeny of a New Species of Hypacrosaurus (Ornithischia, Lambeosauridae) from Montana and Alberta: in Dinosaur Eggs and Babies*, Kenneth Carpenter, Karl Hirsch and John Horner (eds.) Cambridge University Press, New York, 1994) 312–336.
21. Gore, *op. cit.*
22. Glen, William. "What Killed the Dinosaurs?" American Scientist 78:354–370 (1990).
23. Gore, op. cit.; Glen, *op. cit.*

9

PASS THE ROCKS AND TELL ME THE TIME, PLEASE

9.1 TELL ME THE TIME

"What time is it?" is a question that everyone asks. "How old is it?" is another commonly asked question. The time given is not always correct nor the age, when these questions are asked of the earth.

I remember well the occasion when a friend asked me by what means I told how old the earth was and how I told time from the rocks. I was at a loss for words for several minutes, because my friend was not familiar with radiometric dating or its underlying assumptions. It was then that I realised my need to be able to speak "plain language" in order for others to be able to understand what I was trying to say. My answer went something like this:

Whenever I look at the earth and begin to ask time questions, I must first determine if I am addressing the mineral matter of Earth or the past relics of life (fossils), found within the sedimentary layers of Earth. It is very important that this distinction is made first, before any other discussion takes place. Because, if it isn't, there can be room for major misunderstandings! So, let's talk about the mineral matter of Earth first, and then consider the fossils found within Earth.

9.2 SETTING THE RADIOACTIVE CLOCK

The mineral matter of Earth contains many elements that are unstable. These unstable elements change, over time, to other elements which are stable. The unstable elements are called "radioactive elements" or "radioactive isotopes", and the process of changing from unstable elements to stable elements is called "radioactive decay." Many individuals become frightened when they hear the term 'radioactive', because of its association with nuclear bombs, mushroom clouds, and the loss of life or other horrible consequences. The real fact of the matter is, we are surrounded with radioactive isotopes wherever we are, and when we eat we actually ingest the radioactive isotope carbon-14. So, maybe some radioactivity is not frightful or so devastating.

One of the best-known radioactive elements is uranium. Uranium is the element that is used as fuel for the nuclear-power reactors. Another often mentioned radioactive element is plutonium. Plutonium is the major material used in nuclear weapons. If we were able to examine uranium, atom by atom we would notice that all of the uranium atoms do not have the same mass, i.e., some would have a mass of 238 atomic mass units (amu) while others would have a mass of 235 amu. However, they would all be uranium atoms. Atoms of the same element with differing masses are called isotopes. The most abundant isotope of uranium has a mass of 238 amu and we would write it as U^{238}. The isotope used in the power plant reactors is U^{235}. Another well-known radioactive isotope is carbon-14 or C^{14}. Carbon has two stable isotopes, C^{12} and C^{13}, in addition to the radioactive isotope C^{14}.

When a radioactive element decays, a different element is usually formed. The initial unstable isotope is called the parent isotope and the isotopes formed from radioactive decay are called daughter isotopes. A daughter isotope may be another unstable element or a stable element. For example, the stable daughter isotope of U^{238} decay is lead-206 (Pb^{206}). However, many unstable daughter isotopes of U^{238} are produced before Pb^{206} is finally formed. All of the radioactive daughter isotopes, as well as the radioactive parent isotope and the stable daughter isotope, can be mapped out as an isotope decay scheme.

When a radioactive isotope decays, it is characterised by the kind or kinds of radiation it emits, the energy of the particle(s) and the half-life. There are four main types of radioactive decay:

1. Alpha decay (α)
2. Beta decay (β^-)
3. Positron decay (β^+) (sometimes called electron capture)
4. Spontaneous nuclear fission.

The half-life of a radioactive isotope is the length of time that is necessary for the amount of radioactivity (concentration) to decrease by one-half. For example, if we had a radioactive isotope which had a concentration producing 100 disintegrations per minute (dpm), the half-life would be the time needed to fall to a concentration having 50dpm. This time might be as small as one one-thousandth of a second or as long as one billion years! Uranium-238 has a half-life of 4.47 billion years and C^{14} has a half-life of 5,730 years. The isotope of polonium Po^{214} has a half-life of 0.000163 seconds!

The radiometric "clock" is based on the fact that for every parent atom that decays, a stable daughter isotope is formed at the end of the decay scheme, that is, for every "tick" there must be a "tock". For a clock to be "time worthy" it must operate at a constant rate, that is, it cannot lose time and then run fast to catch up.

The radiometric clock is the same – the half-life of the parent isotope must remain constant. The clock mechanism for the radiometric clock is very much like an hourglass. The passage of time is determined by the ratio of the sand in the upper chamber to the sand in the lower chamber. The upper chamber we would call the parent isotope and the lower chamber we would call the daughter isotope.

For the hourglass to be accurate, there can be no addition or subtraction of sand from either of the chambers. Also, if the hourglass is not reset to zero, it is impossible to determine accurately the passage of time, unless the amount of sand in the lower chamber is known and can be subtracted to give the end result.

The same is true for the radiometric clock. The need to prevent addition and subtraction of parent and daughter isotopes from the clock process we call a closed system; and the need to have the lower chamber empty, or its content exactly known before we start timing, we call the zero reset hypothesis.

9.3 USING THE RADIOMETRIC CLOCK

When the scientist knows the half-life, is assured of a closed system, and the zero reset hypothesis has been confirmed, it is possible to determine how long the radiometric clock has been running by measuring the parent-to-daughter isotope ratio. For example, if the parent/daughter ratio is determined to be 1.00, that is, the amount of daughter isotope is equal to the amount of parent isotope, the clock has been running for one half-life. Or, if the parent/daughter ratio determined is 0.125, the clock has been running for three half-lives ($\frac{1}{2} \times \frac{1}{2} \times \frac{1}{2}$). The timing event for the hourglass is a linear function, that is, a straight line, whereas the timing event for the radiometric clock is an exponential function of time, that is, it drops very fast at the beginning and then slowly approaches zero.

If we want to time the cooking of an egg for exactly three minutes, we probably would not use a one-hour hour glass, but rather a miniature hourglass (an egg timer). On the other hand, if we wanted to time the baking of a loaf of bread, we definitely would not use the egg timer but rather the one-hour timer. The same is true for the radiometric clock. To be suitable for dating purposes, the half-life must, on the one hand, be short enough to have produced a measurable amount of daughter isotope since time zero of the sample being studied; on the other hand, it must be long enough for a measurable amount of parent isotope to be still present.

Radioactivity and radiometric dating are still fairly new concepts. Radioactivity has been known only since 1896, and the concept of the radiometric clock was not proposed until 1904 by Lord Rutherford. In 1905, Rutherford, using the ratio of uranium (parent) to helium (α-decay product), proposed that Earth had to be over 2 billion years old. However, the questions of how old Earth is and how old the fossils are were asked long before 1896. Darwin, in 1859, proposed that there had to be at least 300 million years since the end of the Mesozoic (the second major division of the geologic column). Thus, it can be seen that geologic time is not measured in thousands of years, but millions or even billions of years.

If an individual does not have any "time" constraints within his chosen world-view, the most logical choice is to accept the assigned ages for the geologic column as absolute ages. From this choice, the next logical step is to assume that the plant and animal remains found within these layers on Earth, appeared and disappeared at the assigned times. The next step in this logical progression is then to assume that the record of past life, found within these layers, is actually a record of development or evolution. This is a natural conclusion from the logical analyses of the data. It is here, at the logical analyses and the radiometric assumptions, that the "conflict of ages" comes into play.

9.4   RADIOACTIVE TIME VS SCRIPTURAL TIME

Conservative Christians have made the overt choice of accepting the account of Creation, as revealed in a straightforward reading of Scripture. This choice comes with an immediate time constraint, that constraint being a seven-day Creation Week. The Hebrew wording and phraseology leave no room for error, misunderstanding, or reinterpretation; the time frame involved is six literal 24-hour days for the work of Creation and a seventh day added as a day of rest and worship. There is a great difference between 168 hours and 600 Ma (million years) for the development of life! Also, according to the Scriptures, even if the genealogies are rounded off or doubled, the time for life on this planet is in the order of thousands or tens of thousands of years, not millions of years. And yet, even with this great time difference, there is also an interesting similarity between Creation and Evolution. Faith!

At all levels of interpretation of historic time, irrespective of which world-view one adopts, faith is the important factor. The total naturalistic world-view places its faith in human reasoning and time, believing that given enough time and resources, there is no question or problem that cannot be understood. The Scriptural only world-view, places no confidence in science at all, and believes that if we do not understand a problem, or cannot explain some phenomenon, the subject then lies totally in the realm of God. I feel that these two views represent the extremes of an almost continuum of possibilities for a person's world-view. When one adopts a world-view between these extremes, a choice, either consciously or unconsciously, is made, whereby one assigns either science or Scripture as the standard and final arbiter for those areas where the questions and problems are still unresolved.

Our conscious choice, as modern conservative Christians, has been to use Scripture as the final arbiter, but not altogether to abandon science. This choice is not a cop-out, where we dump off all the natty problems on God, but a choice which recognises the strength and limitations of science and the eternal values of Scripture. A choice, which addresses more areas than just the physical world in which we live. A choice not based solely upon human reasoning. Having made this choice, we must then look for alternative interpretations of the fossil record found within Earth's crust.

Looking at the methods used in the radiometric dating of the layers of Earth, we observe two major assumptions that are recognised by the practitioners of radiometric dating as seldom being achieved, namely, complete resetting of the "clock" and the closed system. And yet, modern interpretations of the fossil layer ages seem to ignore these facts and accept, without question, the assigned ages. This bias is not an attempt to deceive but rather the result of a world-view in which there is no time constraint, and hence no need to question the interpretation of the data. Those who see Scripture as relevant in their world-view must search for harmony between the data of science and the revelation of Scripture.

In Genesis 1 and 2 we have a record of the development and great diversity of life, including the unique position held by humans. In Genesis 6 and 7 we have a record of a worldwide Flood that destroyed all life, except that protected by God, and severely altered the surface of the earth. These two sections must go together as an integral package.

The layering of the geologic column from the Flood could answer many perplexing questions posed to the modern geologist. The worldwide distribution of some formations and/or fossil beds cannot be easily explained, if at all, by modern geology. The flat contacts between layers of rocks of supposedly millions of years old, without erosional features, are also problematic. On the other hand, while the exact mechanism cannot be given, it seems possible that a worldwide Flood could account for many of these features, including the layering of the fossils, the widely spread deposits, and the lack of erosional features, all placed in position within a short period of time, rather than millions of years. But what about the ages needed for the development of the various layers? What about the fact that the lower layers seem to date older than the upper layers? Can a worldwide Flood explain these?

No. The worldwide Flood cannot address the millions-of-years question directly. If there is an Achilles heel to the Scriptural interpretation of the geologic column, it has to be the progressive radiometric ages found within the column. Right up front, I must say that I am not aware of a direct linear relationship between the radiometric time sequences for life found within the geologic column, and the Scriptural account of Creation and destruction.

One possible option would be to assume that the mineral matter of Earth is very old, as science suggests; that this matter existed "without form and void" before Creation week, as Scripture may allow (This is in no way supporting the gap theory, which allows for a civilisation in Genesis 1:1, that died out, followed by a gap of millions of years before Creation week began with Genesis 1:2). The long ages for the mineral matter of Earth and the solar system to develop would then be the natural outcome of the radioactive decay processes that have occurred since the creation of the mineral matter "in the beginning" – whenever that was!

The implications of this option would suggest that the radiometric clocks are not reset to zero whenever the minerals are transported by igneous or sedimentary processes. This option also strongly suggests that the radiometric ages assigned to the inorganic minerals associated with a fossil, are more a reflection of the mineral material than an indication of the actual time the fossil was deposited.

The non-reset problems for radiometric ages are not hidden nor are they ignored within the scientific community. This option is simply suggesting that this non-setting of the clock is more the rule, rather than the exception.

9.5 CONCLUSION

Conflicts between the scientific and the Scriptural interpretations of the time record are minimised with this option. However, not all of the questions are answered, and areas of FAITH continue to remain.

What difference does it make as to how old we believe Earth is and life on Earth? It does make a difference. What we believe the ages of Earth and especially life on Earth are, does make a big difference as to how we interpret both science and Scripture.

We must carefully assess the direction in which our decisions, concerning time take us, with respect to our understanding of Scripture and the tenet of our FAITH and world-view as conservative modern Christians. If we find these tenets being undermined and severely called into question because of our position with respect to time issues, we must look for additional insight or simply be willing to say some of the most difficult words known to humans: "I don't know."

Time, as we experience it, is real only because man is finite. However, all aspects of mankind's interpretation of time may not be real. Therefore, we must exercise caution whenever we attempt to enforce a rigid interpretation of a prehistoric phenomenon, irrespective of the source of data, be it science or Scripture.

By the way, "What time is it?" The only rock that I know of that I can trust, is the quartz crystal in my Timex!

10

THE RAINBOW CONNECTION: FOSSILS, THE GEOLOGIC COLUMN AND CALVARY

10.1 FINDING A FOSSIL

Hunting for fossils is great fun, and actually finding one is even better. I remember the thrill of digging for fossils in the United States, high on a hillside in Idaho overlooking the Snake river several hundred metres below. Because fossils do not put up signboards saying, "Dig here if you want to find me," my partner and I agreed that after selecting a spot in which to dig for fossils, we would stay in that same location until we had either found a fossil in that spot or until it was time for our group to return to College. We kept digging, hour after hour, taking turns being in the pit. Nothing was turning up, but we kept to our agreement and did not move to another location. The second day we were still carefully digging in the same spot. Late that afternoon while it was my turn to be in the hole, I recognised that the dirt had an ashen grey, which made me breathe a little faster with anticipation of what I might find. Using my fingers, I carefully scratched here and there at the bottom of the hole and suddenly felt something hard. Scraping away the loose material, I saw a white rounded bone. Removing more of the grey, sandy-like material from the bone caused it to "grow" larger and larger. There before our eyes was a fossil horse or camel skull. We prepared a plaster jacket around the skull and took the treasure back to Walla Walla College, where it can still be seen in the biological museum.

However, digging for and finding fossils, as exciting as it is, forms only part of the story. Interesting and serious questions need to be asked about the fossils themselves. When did all these buried animals live, and how did they all get buried in the layers of the crust of the earth? Above all, do their existence and position in the geologic column, when explained according to Darwinian evolutionary theory, have any potentially negative implications for our Christian faith, particularly concerning our central belief in the atoning power of the precious blood of Jesus? If so, what are some of these implications? And what are some of the possible, reliable solutions to any potential difficulties? This chapter addresses these important questions.

10.2 CONTRASTING VIEWS OF THE GEOLOGIC COLUMN

The crust of our earth constitutes a vast burying-ground for millions of animals which lived, died, and have become entombed in its various stacked upper layers which are called the "geologic column." First it is important to establish that we as Christians do not deny the existence of the fossil-filled geologic column. It is real, beautiful, and awe inspiring, as revealed in the Grand Canyon, Arizona, and other areas of Earth. However, as Christians we embrace a Scripture-inspired interpretation of the formation of the geologic column. This, we know, contrasts with the long-age uniformitarian concept of the cause of the column assumed in evolutionary theory.

Having accepted the reality of the geologic column, we can now raise a potentially serious implication which the column and its fossils have for the central Christian doctrine of the cross of Christ. According to the Darwinian interpretation, the portion of the geologic column containing most of the fossils, formed slowly over a period of approximately 600 million years. Then, and only then, did human beings appear on Earth. Here, a potentially major difficulty arises about Calvary. The Word of God says, in Romans 5:12, "by one man sin entered the world and death by sin," and in Romans 8:20–23, Paul teaches that animal corruption or death first entered the world as the ultimate result of Adam's sin. This means that the Bible teaches that no animals died before Adam's sin, and so, by implication, no animals should appear in the geological column before the existence of human beings. There is a definite theological problem in claiming that animals died before Adam sinned.

10.3 DID ANIMALS DIE BEFORE HUMANS LIVED?

If animals lived and died before Adam's sin, then Adam's sin did not introduce death of any kind into our world, including the death of animals. This admission means that there is no causal connection between sin and death, which is a theologically fatal conclusion, because it means that the death of Christ on the cross is not the wage of sin, therefore, His death saves no one. This conclusion indicates, according to evolutionary theory, how the presence of the fossils in the geologic column can successfully destroy the good news of the forgiveness of sins through the blood of Jesus, thereby destroying our hope of eternal life. This shows just how serious this issue is for all humankind.

Now, we can see the great importance of solving the issue of the remains of dead animals in the geologic column, which lived and died before human beings ever existed. In other words, we can now clearly see that if evolutionary geology is right about the claim that animals have existed for millions of years before the existence of human beings, then evolutionary theory has nullified the heart of the Christian gospel. This serious implication helps to explain why we have young people, in particular, in mind when we write about this vital issue, the relation between science and religion, and its solution. We desire the relationship between geology and Revelation to be one of harmony, not discord, because God is the author of both the natural world and the Scriptures.

How, then, do Christian geologists and theologians explain the presence of all the animals in the geologic column, which are said to have lived and died for millions of years before Adam ever lived and sinned? Perhaps the Bible is not reliable at this point. Perhaps Adam's sin did not result either in his own death or in the death of all the animals. Perhaps the Fall of Adam is not historical at all, but just a myth.

As an initial step in responding to the potential problem noted above, we need to say a bit more about the Darwinian theory of the formation of the fossils and the geologic column, and quote what some other thinkers have said about this potential problem. Contemplating the evolutionary geological point of view, Stephen Jay Gould of Harvard University states that the geologic column began to grow on our planet about 3.75 billion years ago as reflected in the oldest sedimentary rocks represented by the Isua series of west Greenland.[1]

The important point to understand is that the geologic column is said to have grown slowly, little by little, over long ages, rather than all at once. This means that the bottom layers of the column were once the only layers existing, with no other layers of the column resting on top of them. These bottom layers, therefore, lay exposed to the sunlight and weathering processes for millions of years, while animals also lived and died on them. In time, new sediments and dead animals were deposited upon these bottom layers. The more recently deposited layers, in turn, lay exposed for millions of years until additional layers were deposited upon them.

This building pattern of the geologic column continued, according to conventional evolutionary geological theory, for 3.75 billion years, until we have the present geologic column, which can be seen in its most striking reality in the side exposures of the Grand Canyon. Although the process of fossilisation occurred minimally throughout the 3.75 billion years, only during the last 600 million years of the building of the geologic column, commencing with the Cambrian explosion of life forms, have most of the fossilised creatures lived, died, and been entombed. Having described the conventional formation of the geologic column, we can now consider the contrasting reflections of some Christian thinkers, concerning the connection between the geologic column and the work of Christ.

10.4   THE GEOLOGIC COLUMN AND YOUR UNDERSTANDING OF CALVARY

Recently, two fundamentally different kinds of responses to the problem of the column, in relation to Calvary, have been offered by Christian scholars. A first response is presented, for example, by the Christian theologian John Hick, a critical scholar who accepts the macro-evolutionary theory (lower animals evolving into humans). He states that the idea of Adam's fall into sin is not historical, because, "we know today that the conditions that were to cause human mortality [death] were already part of the natural order prior to the emergence of man and prior therefore to any first human sin."[2] His colleague, Karl Schmitz-Moormann, outlines the negative impact this conclusion has upon the traditional account of Calvary: "The notion of [the] traditional view of redemption as reconciliation and ransom from the consequences of Adam's fall is nonsense for anyone who knows about the evolutionary background to human existence in the modern world."[3] What then should the Christian think of redemption? Schmitz-Moormann answers that salvation "cannot mean returning to an original state, but must be conceived as perfecting through the process of evolution."[4] These individuals indicate one response to the geologic column and Calvary. There is, however, another Christian response to which we now turn.

Theologians who accept the historical reliability of the biblical Creation and Flood narratives present a second, but contrasting response to the potentially negative implication, which the fossils in the geological column present concerning Calvary. First, these scholars clearly outline the difficulty. For example, in an article written in 1994 and entitled, "Theological Problems with Theistic Evolution", David H. Lane writes: "Theistic evolution denies the doctrine of sin as the cause for physical death, which has its basis in the historical truth of the Fall. It thereby destroys the basis of the doctrines of Christ's substitutionary atonement and redemption of sinners."[5] Christian scholar, Nigel M. de S. Cameron, recently and powerfully addressed this same problem by arguing that were Adam subject to physical death before his sin, this evolutionary conclusion would "overthrow the sin death causality, and in so doing pulls the rug from under the feet of the evangelical understanding of the atonement."[6] Finally, Marco Terreros is the first Christian scholar to formulate a Ph.D. dissertation dealing precisely with this topic. Writing in his work entitled, "Death Before the Sin of Adam: A Fundamental Concept in Theistic Evolution and Its Implications for Evangelical Theology", Terreros observes that:

The origin of animal death as well as human death is linked exclusively to human sin, which means that human and animal death cannot be separated as consequences of sin. Thus, evangelical scholars who accept animal death as occurring before the sin of our first parents necessarily nullify, from a biblical point of view, the causal link between death and human sin required in historic atonement theology.[7]

The efforts of this second group of Christian scholars show that the geologic column, as conventionally interpreted, has fatal implications for Calvary, as traditionally understood. They also point out encouraging biblical and geological responses to the challenge presented to the cross of Christ by the presence of fossils in the geologic column, allegedly existing before the existence of human beings. We turn to the work of these scholars below.

In response to the difficulty noted above, Richard Davidson introduces the biblical teaching of the Flood and its extent. Davidson underscores the biblical teaching of the universality of the Flood, as presented in the narrative of Genesis 6–9.[8] In other words, here is where the rainbow connection begins to enter our discussion, as a biblical answer to the fatal difficulty outlined above. The Bible teaches that because of the great sins of human beings, God sent a world-destroying Flood that was universal, not local, to eradicate the unrepentant inhabitants of the earth in addition to destroying the face of the earth itself. The Hebrew word for the Flood, used in Genesis 6–9, is a very special word, mabbul, implying a heavenly ocean which is used of no other Flood in the Bible. The Genesis Flood is not an ordinary, local, repeatable flood. Rather, the mabbul of Genesis occurs when the "floodgates of the sky were opened" (Genesis 7:11), and water came down from the sky while water came up from the ground. Thus, the extremely important conclusion is that Genesis clearly teaches that the Flood, or mabbul, is the cosmic or universal undoing of a universal Creation structure. This structure was established on the second day of Creation when

God separated the waters "which were below the expanse from the waters which were above the expanse: and it was so" (Genesis 1:7). The Flood is the undoing of this Creation structure. This truth is also pointed out vividly by critical scholar Gerhard von Rad as follows:

Mabbul ... is a technical term for a part of the world structure, namely, the heavenly ocean ... which empties downward through latticed windows ... [We] must understand the Flood, therefore, as a catastrophe involving the entire cosmos ... a destruction of the entire cosmic system... The two halves of the chaotic primeval sea, separated – the one up, the other below – by God's creative government (Genesis 1.7-9), are again united; creation begins to sink again into chaos. Here the catastrophe, therefore, concerns not only men and beasts ... but the earth (Genesis 6:13; 9.11) – indeed, the entire cosmos.[9]

The fact, indicated here, that the Flood is the cosmic undoing of Creation, is a powerful truth and is the greatest reason for showing why a local flood concept should not be accepted, because a local flood cannot undo the divinely established universal Creation structure as required by the biblical text. This conclusion shows why, historically, a local flood theory cannot do justice to what the Bible has in mind when it speaks about the Flood in which Noah was involved. We turn to a discussion of the theological importance of this result.

The conclusion that the Genesis Flood is indeed a historical, universal – rather than a local geological – phenomenon is vital for our discussion, because a universal Flood can produce the universal geologic column, whereas a local flood cannot produce a universal geologic column. A universal Flood, as described in Genesis 6–9, can act as the geological engine in forming the major portion of the universal geologic column. The important implication is that a universal Flood would have the power to introduce and quickly entomb dead animals in deposits which now form the present geologic column, after the introduction of sin and death into the world by Adam. This means that a universal Flood acts to preserve the causal connection between sin and death, thus safeguarding the continuing power of the blood of Christ to forgive sins. This shows the importance which the geological fact of a universal Flood has for the continuing truth of Calvary. Moreover, this profound theological importance which the global Flood has for the cross of Christ is the basic reason why this book presents chapters from a geological point of view, presenting field evidence which is consistent with the kind of geological effects which would be expected in a deluge on the scale indicated in Genesis 6–9. This leads to a discussion below of the origin and message of the rainbow.

10.5   THE RAINBOW CONNECTION

Standing on the Kaibab layer and looking northward across the wide abyss of the Grand Canyon, one can see more stacked sedimentary layers of the geologic column in the single exposure sequence, than are visible in any other column exposure on earth. The sheer magnitude of the scene generates the irrepressible question, How were these massive sedimentary layers formed, in which countless fossils are entombed? A powerful biblical and geological response to this query resides in the covenant sign given to Noah, at times displayed in awe-inspiring majesty over the Grand Canyon (see front cover). For the visitor fortunate enough to stand at the rim of the Grand Canyon after a rainstorm and in the right atmospheric conditions, a rainbow can be seen arching in brilliant colours against a dark sky. There is a grand connection between this rainbow, the formation of the Grand Canyon, and Calvary.

At the end of the world-wide Flood, God attached a very important significance to the beautiful rainbow, in these words: "I establish My covenant with you; and all flesh shall never again be cut off by the water of the flood, neither shall there again be a flood to destroy the earth…. I do set My bow in the cloud, and it shall be for a sign of a covenant between Me and the earth" (Genesis. 9:11, 13). This means that the beautiful rainbow bending over the Grand Canyon has become a "sign".

The message of the rainbow for the theologian and geologist viewing the layers of the geological column at the Grand Canyon, or anywhere else, is that these exposed layers were not formed over billions of years. They were formed relatively rapidly by means of a divinely initiated, unimaginably violent, cosmic-wide Flood, described in Genesis 6–9.

God deliberately made the rainbow His memorial of this universal Flood and attached to the rainbow the message that such a mega-aquatic disaster would never occur again. So, to the inquiring geologist standing at the rim of the Grand Canyon who may wonder, "How were these layers formed?" God says to him, "Look up when you see a rainbow arching over the Grand Canyon, observe its beauty and believe its message. My answer to your understandable question is written there in the sky."

The most important message of the rainbow is theological. The deeper implied communication of the beautiful, bending bow is that because the great energy of the Flood formed the geologic column rapidly (at a time after the fall of Adam and Eve), the causal connection between sin and death is preserved, thereby establishing that the blood of Christ has not lost its atoning power. This is the greatest message of the rainbow, and one which creates a most important connection between it, Calvary, fossils, and the stacked sedimentary layers of the geologic column. Thank God for the deep geological and theological significance of the bow. These are the reasons for saying that "with a rainbow over the Grand Canyon, God says it all."

10.6   CONCLUSION

In summary, every time we see a rainbow, God wants us to remember at least three things: We are to recall that God sent a worldwide Flood which destroyed earthly vegetation, beasts, birds, unrepentant humanity, and the crust of the earth itself. Also that a worldwide Flood of water will never come again onto this earth.

The Flood serves as a symbol of a future worldwide judgement of this earth by fire. Thus, the rainbow should remind us that a universal Flood did occur in the past, after Adam sinned, and was powerful enough to sort out and entomb very rapidly the dead animals into the geological column. This means that a universal Flood, symbolised by the rainbow, preserves the connection between human sin and human death, and is also the connection between human sin and the death of animals. Best of all, the universal Flood safeguards the atoning value of the death of Jesus for the forgiveness of our sins. This establishes a most important connection between the rainbow, Calvary, and the stacked sedimentary layers of the geologic column. As the title of this book suggests, the earth and sky are indeed speaking forcefully and clearly, in support of the truth, not only of Biblical history but also of the forgiveness of our sins.

Please join us in praising God for the deep geological and theological significance of the rainbow.

References
1.   Gould, Stephen Jay. *Wonderful Life: The Burgess Shale and the Nature of History*. (New York: W.W. Norton, 1989), 57.
2.   Hick, John. *Evil and the God of Love*. (London: Macmillan, 1966), 285

3. Quoted in Hans Küng, Gedo (New York, 1993), 22.
4. Schmitz-Moormann, Karl. "Evolution and Redemption: What is the Meaning of Christians Proclaiming Salvation in an Evolving World?" *Progress in Theology* 1:2 (June 1993); 7.
5. Lane, David H. "Theological Problems with Theistic Evolution," Part II, *Bibliotheca Sacra 50* (April–June 1994): 170.
6. Cameron, Nigel M. de S. *Evolution and the Authority of the Bible* (Greenwood, S.D.: The Attic Press, 1983), 52.
7. Terreros, Marco T. "Death Before the Sin of Adam: A Fundamental Concept in Theistic Evolution and Its Implications for Evangelical Theology" (Ph.D. diss., Andrews University, Seventh-day Adventist Theological Seminary, 1994), 227.
8. Davidson, Richard M. "Biblical Evidence for the Universality of the Genesis Flood," a paper read before the Evangelical Theological Society's National Meeting, November 18, 1994, Lisle-Naperville, Illinois, particularly p16.
9. von Rad, Gerhard. *Genesis* (Philadelphia: The Westminster Press, 1972), 128.

INDEX

D